www.noirblancetc.com • editionsnoirblancetc@gmail.com

The United States Copyright Office Registration # TXu 1-858-671

ISBN: 978-9953-986-01-2
Printed in Beirut, Lebanon
First Edition: 2018

Published by:
Noir Blanc Et Caetera s.a.r.l.

Layout : Jessie Raphaël Bali.

Ibrahim Lahoud & Jad Lahoud

102

BROTHERHOOD FORTITUDE PURPOSE

A story of war and reconciliation

**A HISTORIC FICTION – MEMOIR
BASED ON ACTUAL EVENTS**

To
NADIM AND NADIA
our beloved Father and Mother

To
TONY ASMAR (Bozo)
and
SELIM ABDO (Sierra)
never forgotten

To
our beautiful children
NADIM, SABINE, AND JOY-JUDE
so you never forget

MESSAGE TO OUR DEAR READERS

In order to preserve the integrity of our stories, minimal contextual editing has been performed. Each of us used our own tone of voice and style in our book. We trust that this approach will help to reveal a clear insight into our personalities, perspectives, feelings, and state of mind throughout our book.

Please forgive any linguistic imperfection or unconventional vocabulary. We are confident that reading the book will transcend the boundaries of language and grammar, and become an intimate, and life changing experience.

Ibrahim Lahoud and Jad Lahoud

WHAT IS 102?

When the Lebanese Red Cross established centers across Lebanon, it gave serial numbers based on the region followed by the center's locale. For example, number 1 was used for the Beirut region, and every center was numbered subsequently 101, 102, etc. If another Region was assigned the number 2, the centers would be numbered 201, 202, etc.

While 101 was located in the Western part of Beirut, 102 was the center located in the Eastern part of Beirut. Both parts of the Capital were divided by the war front, the so-called Green Line.

NOTE : Most of the original names and call signs have been changed to preserve the identity and privacy of the persons in the book. The stories in the book were all written based on our personal recollection and interpretations to the best of our knowledge.

PROLOGUE

War and reconciliation never went in tandem. Struggle and defeat pair well with compromise. Finding one's inner peace in times of war can seldom be achieved alone. The dark thoughts that rule our deepest darkness could not fathom the breadth of the task. Our lost souls would find solace only in an alter ego.

This is the story about two alter egos, children of a fait accompli; offspring of circumstances who grew in a civil war waged against compromise, society, and family. Becoming what you planned for yourself instead of what your entourage concocted for you is a battle to end all battles.

102 is a story about things gone wrong and where, as in real life, happy endings are not always the right endings. It is a story of two fatherless boys, reconciling with themselves at first and then with a harsh reality dictating a path to disaster and failure. 102 is an alternative interpretation of "self-made", a depiction of how moral wealth outweighs material wealth. It is a tale about keeping your nose above the water in an ocean infested with sharks.

102 is the story of two young men who succeed at pushing their limits, going beyond the social, familial, and professional contexts. It's the story of two adolescents who believed they could achieve their ultimate dream whatever the cost.

102 is about two brothers, Ibrahim (Eby) and Jad, torn by opposite personalities, victimized by an absurd civil war; but inseparably bonded by fraternal love, altruistic compassion and the realization that lost souls find solace in their alter ego or partner. They woke up to the Lebanese Civil War in April of 1975, lost and disoriented. Their father died young, while they were aged 12 and 8. Their mother, who was 39 then, now faces the daunting task of raising two young men amidst a civil war where money is scarce, temptation is strong, and every step along the way is a death wish.

On that April day, Eby and Jad witnessed their present disintegrate and their future slowly dim to oblivion. They are both now strenuously striving to lay the foundation for a life. They have no choices, nowhere to go, and no one to talk to.

Handicapped by a dysfunctional home, governed by a patriarchal family, and earmarked by a cruel entourage, they are sailing against the wind and odds. Their once discordant paths converge at the Lebanese Red Cross when Jad decides to quit fighting with the local militia and Eby refuses to get drafted.

102 is the Lebanese Red Cross Center to which they both were assigned, in different teams. There, they discover a purpose, a mission. They both have a creed now, a family, and a reason to sail across the war. Exposed to every possible emotion one can experience, they bear witness to war, death, tears, pain, and love. They console nervous breakdowns and soldiers crying. They bond with newfound friends and go on impossible missions.

102 is a story about paradoxes. On one end is a path

of hope delivered by every mission they both undertake. On the other end is a path of uncertainty, a path devoid of aspiration. With every mission that saves a life comes another day that places the two young men far from a future, far from their true potential, and far from the normalcy an adolescent should be looking forward to.

Although the definition of "self-made" has gained its own stereotype, Eby and Jad had (and still do today) a different interpretation for it, a better rendition of a self-made man. For them it was never about success: they do not acknowledge having succeeded, but rather they acknowledge the genesis and trajectory forged on one's own terms and resources. Whatever they achieved so far, they achieved it relying on the unique wealth they possessed: their will and resolve.

Robert Alden said: *"There is no darkness in the whole universe deep enough to dim the light of the faintest candle"*.

Dad at the beach with two of his friends sitting in a way that hides his amputated leg.

OF FATHERS, TRAMS,
AND COURAGE
1950

Nadim is 22 years old. A heart-throb with an almost obsessive desire for elegance, all the girls of Gemmayzeh lust for a piece of him. He and his close friend Mazen are boarding the tramway from the Bourj Square in downtown Beirut to Gemmayzeh, where Nadim lives. Mazen and Nadim are only separated by different jobs. The rest of the time, they always hang out together.

To allow a swift loading and unloading of passengers, tramways traveling at slow speeds do not have doors. In the crowded city of Beirut where tourists, businesses,

A tramway car in beirut in the 60's, similar to the one dad fell under and lost his leg.

and the rural exodus converge, trams are always packed. Passengers hop on and off while the cab is moving. They stand on the metal doorstep and hold onto the guiding handle. Mazen is in this position with Nadim next to him, one step above.

As they reach The Sacred Heart College, Mazen suddenly loses his grip and starts falling off the tram's doorstep. He vainly tries to reach for the handle just as Nadim jumps out while firmly holding the guiding rail with his left hand, reaches down as far as he could, grabs Mazen's right arm, and abruptly pulls him in. At that very second, Mazen falls inside the tram's cabin, the momentum's thrust sends Nadim falling out. He hits the pavement on his left shoulder, rolls on his back, and his right leg slides between the tram's steel wheels and rails.

Nadim does not stand a chance. The massive metallic wheel has a thin protruding edge that locks inside the grooved rail. It acts like a blade and slices away Nadim's leg.

At 22 Nadim (who few years from now will become our father), the handsome heart-throb of the neighborhood, loses his leg right above the knee - and nearly his life - trying to save his best friend. For that, everyone respects him deeply.

Now, Dad wears a prosthetic leg, a state-of-the-art piece of technology for the era, but his limp, coupled with his legendary elegance, becomes a trademark.

(Eby)
AN END AND A BEGINNING.
LIVING AS AN ORPHAN
1972

I am standing on the balcony. It is early afternoon on a sunny and relatively warm February Monday. This is my favorite pastime; just leaning over with my elbows on the cold steel rails and watching the docking and departing boats in the Port of Beirut and the freight locomotive trains steam their way across the main road and inside the Port's cargo station.

I have an unobstructed view of the whole coastal region. To my right, I can see the Bay of Jounieh and all the way to the shores of Byblos, the oldest city on earth. The Mediterranean shore is crowned by Mount Lebanon that rises as high as a mile, covered with pristine white snow. Lebanon's name comes from the Phoenician roots *"Lbn"* (pronounced laban) which means "white", in reference to its snow-capped peaks.

Facing the balcony, the Port of Beirut stands out with the azure Mediterranean Sea as backdrop. I watch the horizon every evening hugging the sea in a beautiful display of sunset colors. Every New Year's Eve, all the boats in the Port blow endless whistles and shoot flares in the sky. It was a 12-year-old boy's best show on Earth.

I can never forget the breathtaking sight. To this day, it still brings back memories, both vividly peaceful and disturbing.

Mom took my younger brother Jad to the dentist. I am waiting for Dad, taking his usual afternoon nap, to wake up and help me with my homework. I am in sixth grade and doing very well so far at school. Dad holds a prestigious position at the Ministry of Education, where he is Head of the Youth and Sports directorate, a position he earned after years of teaching in public schools and struggling up the ladder. He is much respected among his peers, family, and friends. The family's youngsters love my Dad Nadim's sense of humor.

I look at my watch, an Edox given to me by my godfather three years ago. It is 3:45 p.m., the time Dad usually wakes up. He is very punctual. I choose to wait for a while despite my impatience. At 3:50 p.m., I decide to wake him up. I walk into my parents' bedroom sit next to Dad on the bed. He is sleeping with his back facing me. I gently shake his shoulder while calling him. Nothing! I shake him once more and call his name.

He used to play pranks on Jad and me, lying on the floor and playing dead. We used to freak out at first, but things always ended with a good laugh. The last memory I have of that game is from the days of the old house in Gemmayzeh. We had to move to the current one after Dad had a mild stroke and was forbidden from climbing stairs. The old World War II-era building did not have elevators, and Dad used to climb three stories with his prosthetic leg. It was on a Christmas Eve, and Dad decided to play dead right by the Christmas tree while we were opening our presents. Jad and I screamed with terror first, then delight over my Father's sneaky playfulness, and laughed about it for the rest of the night.

Today, something is not right. I start to feel anxious and

nervous. I hold my Father's right forearm and roll him to face me. His skin is ice cold. He immediately falls on his back motionless. I look at his face. His eyes are slightly open, with a chilling empty stare. His lips are blue. I am 12 years old, too young to read the telltale signs. I remain on the bed beside my father, wondering what to do. Oddly enough I am more puzzled than scared, but something is telling this is no game. In some odd way, I know what is happening; yet I have difficulty reconciling my emotions with my perceptions.

Jad will turn 9 in less than a month from now. He will miss his Dad celebrating his birthday. In fact, he is not going to celebrate at all. That day, my brother will not get a birthday cake or gifts. Christmases would never be the same for Jad and me. There would be no Christmas trees, no Christmas joy, and no Christmas gifts for quite a while.

The sound of the house door slamming startles me. Mom and Jad are back from the dentist. I stand up and walk out slowly, as if I did not want to wake Dad up, and stand at the room door. Calmly I say, *"Mom, I don't know what's wrong with Dad."*

From then on, things happen in a different space-time continuum. Mom looks at me first, and I can see the expression on her face change. She walks slowly at first, then faster, still holding her purse and umbrella. It seems like a long uninterrupted shot from a Hitchcock movie. As she gets closer to me, I can see her face already displaying panic and fear. She has a begging look in her eyes, staring at me as if she is asking *"Eby? What are you telling me?"* She walks past me, while still staring into my eyes, and steps inside the room. Jad follows, clueless.

She stands by the door with her hand on the door frame, fearing to get closer. She looks at her husband, then walks closer and bends over him. Her eyes are now open wide with a look of dismay and panic I will never forget. She puts the palm of her hand on his cheek and pulls it back abruptly. Her face freezes and she lets out a long strident scream, shouting his name so loud, so desperately, that I understand. I understand what I have dreaded.

– *Nadiiiiiiiiiiim!*

Nadia lets herself fall over him, hugging him, and repeatedly calling his name.

Mom is completely disoriented now. Nadim was much more than a husband; he literally was managing her life and ours. Now, Nadia has to be both a mother and father despite the docile housewife she has always been. However, that was never Mom's forte. She cannot and will never be able to be a father. The consequence was obvious; replacing Dad with her family, letting them become the father we had just lost. You only have to imagine the results.

I just stand there, numb. Jad runs to the other side of the bed, sits next to our father, holds his cold cheeks, and screams at me. "*Go get him a glass of water! Go! Go!*"

I run to the kitchen, open the fridge and pour a cold glass of water thinking how come Jad, only 8 then, thought of it and I did not. I know that Dad loves his water freezing cold. I rush back, but stop and remain standing at the door of the room holding the glass. The three of us don't know what to do. We never faced a similar situation before. Even if we had, Jad and I were too scared to do anything. Mom, between sobs, whispers at me to go knock next door and ask Nelly, our Egyptian neighbor, to come over. I don't remember much from there on.

I think we should talk about how they took us downstairs to the neighbors and how they told us that Dad was sick and the ambulance came to take him to the hospital. After that night we went to our Aunt Marie-Rose's house.

Nadim, our father, was 42 years old. He died from an acute brain thrombosis.

Today, 10 years later, I know exactly what to do.

(Eby)
A PEACE STRANGER THAN LIFE
1973

We were not allowed to attend our father's funeral service. For me now, this was a display of pure backwardness and lack of understanding of how important closure is. We were too young they said. Because of this never had proper closure with my father's death. I can confidently say that neither did Jad.

It took me a year to reconcile with the fact that I no longer had a father. I kept living in denial punctuated by brief 'awakenings' when I was aware of the truth. I wrote a poem for my Dad. As I read it today, it was not bad for a 12-year-old boy. This is the proof of how powerful my emotions were during one of my 'awakenings.' This is how that French poem ended:

Je viens aux portes du printemps arroser de mes larmes
La terre des catacombes, froide, à geler les âmes.
Et mélangées aux senteurs de ta beauté qui va au seuil,
Sans tristesse, sans regrets, sans deuil
Font pousser entre le gazon et demain
Des trèfles à quatre feuilles...

("Here I am, standing at the doorstep of spring
To water with my tears, the soil upon your grave;
So cold, it freezes the soul.
And mixed to the scent of your beauty going
to the edge,

Without sadness, without regrets, without mourning,
Blossom between the grass and tomorrow
Four-leaved clovers")

I started writing poems, most of which express my anger with time and destiny. I cocooned myself in my own space, reading a lot, drawing, assembling jigsaw puzzles, and making military model kits. I became a recluse, in a room populated by impossible dreams, sinister nightmares, and model kits of tanks and planes.

By now, I can feel my reality change. I fail my sixth grade, and Jad fails his third; this is the first time ever we both fail at school. My classmates' attitudes shift; I feel more like an outcast. I spend recess walking alone across the playground, drowning in my thoughts – so much so that one day I trip on a rope and lose consciousness. I remember waking up at the infirmary.

With a deteriorating school record, my hopes are rushing downhill. I do have moments where I sit and think about my future, but that only lasts for short periods of time because there is not much to think about. It is a fact that I am going nowhere, and I most certainly will never be the architect I dream of becoming.

Even my family's attitude takes a turn. I am no longer – and neither is Jad – looked at as the sons of Nadim and Nadia, but rather as the two poor little boys without a father. Given that my uncles take charge of our family's finances, the idea of being ever grateful to them and their family is solidly anchored in our little heads. I feel like an underdog in the presence of cousins. The sense of being a rat within a pack of lions is overwhelming.

As I reach eighth grade, even I wonder how I made it this

far. I don't like school; I haven't liked it ever since my Dad's passing. I don't feel it teaches me anything meaningful. Most of what I know today was never bestowed upon me by the Lebanese educational system. All that I have learned is the result of my own efforts, readings, and research.

Now, I am faced with the ultimate decision of how to continue my education. I have four choices: Math, Science, Literature or Commercial Sciences. As far as I am concerned, they sounded more like having no choice at all. I am persuaded by my mother's brothers to pursue the Commercial Sciences route, as that plan a Technical Baccalaureate within a swift three years. After that, I can start looking for a job.

Commercial Sciences sound more like Chinese to me. After two painful years, Brother Fidèle (then the dean) congratulates me for having failed all major courses including Math, Financial Math, and Accounting; and with grades he has never witnessed in his 40-year career... and he fires me.

I change schools and move to the Lebanese Center for Commercial Sciences, a small technical school with a big name in Gemmayzeh, less than a minute away from home. I am still wide-eyed at how I manage to make it through the remaining two years and two grueling Baccalaureate exams. It is through abundant cheating and a lot of divine intervention that I manage to earn my degree. It is now May of 1978.

Me at one of the training camps.

(Jad)
STRANGER IN MY OWN HOME
1972

I was 14 years old, lying down by the sandbags, the barrel of my M16 resting in the small slit. On the other side, I could see the giant Somali maybe 50 yards away. I'd been instructed to aim for the head, neck, and chest, and shoot only three bullets at a time. Ammunition was in short supply. Fighters were given only four magazines per shift. This was the first time I'd ever pointed a gun at a human being.

It was 10:00 a.m., and I should have been at school that day. I was in eighth grade, the perfect alibi for my mother and brother. For a moment, I wondered how the hell I got myself into this situation.

I dropped out of school at an early age. I barely finished the ninth grade when I gave up. After my Dad's demise and returning to school, I felt like an outcast. Everyone was staring at me with a mixture of pity and quandary. I could even hear my classmates whisper to each other about me being an orphan. Worried about Eby and me, Mom agreed to have the School Psychologist and Social Assistant have a chat with us and help us go through the ordeal of losing our father. To me, that made things even worse as it hampered my reintegration. I started having suicidal ideas, at times convinced that if I died I would go to heaven and see Dad. I must have voiced it one day, because later that year I had a parade of shrinks, priests, and family all taking a shot at convincing me to live life and forget about my dark ideas.

My dream was to become a commercial pilot, but when I tried to discuss it with my Uncle, the only thing that flew away was my dream. He told me in a long sermon that I should stick with him and learn the business of selling clothes, so I could make a living soon – rather than wasting my time and his money learning how to fly airplanes. One of my favorite pastimes was when Dad used to take Eby and me to the airport to watch the planes take off and land. These were happy days, worry-free; the word "terrorism" was never used and airports had wide balconies overlooking the runways. The glamour of watching the aircraft gracefully land, the stylish crew walking in teams, and the travelers boarding was a treat to me. I used to spend hours at home sitting on a low rattan stool on the balcony watching planes flying in from the horizon over the Mediterranean and toward the airport to my left. Just as I used to watch them vanish behind the battle-scarred downtown Beirut, I saw my dream of becoming a pilot wither away.

My uncles are successful manufacturers and wholesalers of wool clothing and apparel. They supply most of the upscale clothing shops in Beirut and even in neighboring countries. During the war, sales plummeted and they ended up closing the factory. One of them, who is more on the import-export side, kept the business running, transforming his once successful clothing shop into an office and warehouse, catering to his wholesale business.

His shop is coincidentally located on the ground floor of the building where both Eby and I were born, and where we lived on the second floor until 1970 when our father, 40 years old then, had a mild stroke and was strictly forbidden from climbing stairs and was instructed by doctors to move to an apartment building with elevators. This is when we rented the apartment on the parallel street of Gemmayzeh facing the Beirut Port.

My uncle made me work even on Saturdays, and I had to watch my friends pass by the shop on their way to the beach while I was busy washing my uncle's car. He was very picky and a seasoned businessman who was hardened by time. For him, family is one thing, but business a totally different turf; and he makes that quite clear to me. What hurt me the most is the way he put other employees ahead of his own family. Among other rules, during office hours I was not allowed to call him "Uncle", it had to be Mister.

Unfortunately, our paternal grandmother decided not to support us financially, in fact not even emotionally. Our Uncle Samir, the younger brother of my father, passed a few months after my Dad; it was a horrific freak car accident in

Yemen. He was supposed to take care of us financially and assume the role of my late father. His passing was not only tragic due to his very young age, but also because of the wife and three young kids he left behind. "Ammo", Uncle Samir, was a successful General Contractor and a very funny and loving person. When Father passed away, he was there for us (for the very short time he was alive). Before leaving for his trip to Yemen, he came home and told my mother not to ever worry! He was working on a big deal that would make him a lot of money and would allow him to build two homes next to each other, one for them and one for us, and that he would take care of us all. Life dealt us another hard blow with "ammo" Samir's demise.

Eby was never gifted for Commercial Sciences. In fact, he had no idea of how to buy a pound of tomatoes. My mother would give him LBP 10 (Lebanese Pounds) to buy a kilo of tomatoes. He would come back within minutes, put the bag of tomatoes on the kitchen table, and hand her the change. When she asked him the cost, he always responded with something like, "*I don't know. I gave the guy the LBP 10 and he returned to me the change that I gave you.*"

On the other hand, when my mother asked me to do the same, I would go around the entire neighborhood looking for the cheapest pound of tomatoes, bargain with the guy for an hour to get an LBP 1 discount. When I got home, I made sure to let my mother know that I was able to get her the best price, and that I deserved to keep the change.

(Eby)
PLANNING A LIFE AND MAKING IT WORK
1978

On this Friday, November 10, 1978, I met Aline, my wife-to-be. Well, I did meet her once before, but it was just a small chat during an outing with friends. She told me then that she is studying to become an Interior Designer. On that November day, I thought I would meet her again to inquire on what it takes to join the same university. I always wanted to become an architect and dreamed of going to university, but never got the chance. I still do today. Since Dad died, my uncles were kind enough to take us under their wings and pay for my and Jad's schooling. But going to university was not an option. Since I was 10 years old, I used to draw buildings on large sheets of graph paper that Dad brought me from work. I copied existing buildings and created new ones. I still have some of those drawings today. Then I started buying architecture magazines and spending hours reading them and copying featured blueprints on tracing paper.

Aline shares my passion for music and plays the guitar. I ask her if she could teach me and she agrees. I play the harmonica well, another passion I inherited from my father. He played the accordion and harmonica too. So, Aline and I started meeting and playing music.

Through my Scout days, I made some friends with whom I kept in touch. They introduce me to their own circle, most of which are musicians. We decide to form a band, called Sirocco. Aline and I are the lead singers and we start rehearsing in a warehouse provided by the drummer's father. Later, we move to the Lazarists School in Ashrafieh, where the monks are kind enough to lend us one of their many underground halls.

The leader of the band, a charismatic self-appointed alpha male of this group of friends, introduces me to his uncle, René, who owns the then highly popular "Flash" children magazine. Every afternoon at 4:00 p.m., I walk from home to René's in Ashrafieh's Sassine Square, where the small team of three, an Editor, a Graphic Designer, and me, work in the dining room. Every day, I finish school at 2:00 p.m., go home for a quick lunch and head on foot to work at "Flash". Most of the time, it's only me there. The Editor and Graphic Designer pass by occasionally to deliver their material. I stay at work until 7:00 p.m. or 8:00 p.m. and then walk back home. René gave me a copy of the house key, so all I have to do when he and his wife are not home, is switch off the lights and lock the door behind me. René is a nice old man who had the idea of starting up a small magazine for teens filled with games and news, but the innovative concept that made "Flash" so successful is the covers of the magazine. They were made up of stickers, tens of them covering the front and back covers. Even the logo was a sticker. Most issues were already sold out before hitting the bookstores. The stickers are the work of the designer, Johnny. I hate him. No, he has never done anything to hurt me; as a matter of fact, he is a nice and very talented young man. I hate him for the name he carries. Remember when Dad lost his leg in a freak tramway accident while helping his friend from falling under the tram's wheels? Mazen is the grandfather of Johnny.

Now you tell me, what are the odds? I just hate Johnny and cannot help it. I came to find out who he was simply because his family name is not a widely spread one. After I met Johnny, I waited for a couple of months before approaching him and asking if he was related to Mazen.

At Christmas in 1978, Aline and I are doing well, very well. I take her out to dinner on December 23rd and declare my love for her. She reciprocates.

The same week, I graduated with a Technical Baccalaureate in Accounting. I land a job as a paste-up artist in a small, obscure advertising agency, which is conveniently located a block away from home. How I shifted from Commercial Sciences to Graphic Design is another divine intervention. A friend of the family who saw my drawings and my potential introduced me to the agency owner.

Later, I manage to grow into a Graphic Designer and Art Director for two of Lebanon's largest advertising agencies, in 1980 and 1982. I was never gifted for Commercial Sciences, and could never imagine myself as a teller in a bank.

I see circumstances and events happening in my life as scenes, shocking beginnings, and dramatic endings. I listen to cool and slow music, and I slowly get introduced to Jazz. Every tune is a scene from a movie, where some make me cry, while others make me go out on the balcony and look at the Port of Beirut, the sea, and the mountains and wait for the end credits. It is six years after Dad's death and my life is taking a bizarre turn. I wait anxiously but patiently for my closure and happy ending.

The infamous war-front green line separating east from west beirut.

(Jad)
AT WAR WITH MYSELF
1976

When I was 13 years old, I thought war was fun and I believed it was my duty to defend my country. Fighting makes you a man, a feared bully, or so I thought; but it was not only that. In their recruiting efforts, the militiamen played their role to perfection. They convinced me and other boys from the neighborhood that by joining the war, we were complying, we were fitting in, and we were doing the right thing.

Living in a neighborhood bordering a war front, the only people you meet are militiamen and fighters.

That's where I met and befriended Elie and Michel. Elie oversaw one part of the "Souks" (the market place) front in downtown Beirut.

It was January in 1977, two months before my 14th birthday. I got my fair share of indoctrination about why I should fight and defend my neighborhood and country; although I didn't need much. Coupled with my thrill for war, it was all I needed to hear. In the blink of an eye, I was at the Phalangists' party headquarters completing an apprentice's first task: filling M16, FAL, and AK-47 magazines. I was also wrapping ham and cheese sandwiches to be sent to the fighters on the front line. This was the job description: do whatever has to be done.

Within a few months, I had displayed such dedication and passion that they sent me on a training round at the Don Bosco monastery. After three months of intense and grueling boot camp, I was dispatched to my first tour of duty. I spent most of my time stationed at the unfinished concrete shell of a building on the Beirut Green Line front, which we nicknamed the *Baneyet el Baton*, which literally means "shell building". It was so strategically located that the Phalangists could not afford to lose it.

Against the sandbag bunker at the bottom of the *Baneyet el Baton*, I was kneeling with my M16, aiming at a Somali giant. Elie and Michel spotted the Somali on the other side of the front, and they thought he could be my ideal inaugural shot. There were many Somali mercenaries during the war fighting along the other side.

– *Come on, Jad. Take your shot. Aim at the head, shoot, then the neck, shoot, and then the chest. Boom!* Elie says. *Three shots only. Kill him cold or he will kill you.*

– *These motherfuckers don't die,* added Michel. *One bullet will never do. Make sure the three bullets hit him from the head down. Those bastards have the luxury and the money to wear bulletproof jackets.*

Remorse, regrets, and all sorts of sorry feelings rushed through my head. As I aimed at the man's head, I thought about God, going to hell when I die, and my Mother's teachings about respecting life. My fear of shooting someone in cold blood overwhelmed me now. All the indoctrinating talk I'd heard in the past, how "fighting makes you a man, a feared bully" vanished into thin air. Now I was sick, dizzy, and sweating.

– *Fire man, fucking fire!* shouted Elie. *If you don't kill him, he will kill us all!*

I hesitated.

– *Fuck you!* screamed Michel. *Fire now or leave the front for good and go back to your mama, ya hmar! You jackass.*

I slowly lowered my M16, aimed at the Somali's thigh, and shot. Once. The giant man fell; but within five seconds, he stood up, pointed his Kalashnikov toward our bunker, and fired until he ran out of ammo.

I was still aiming through the hole in the sandbags, frozen and numb. I knew I had just shot him. I saw him fall. Michel snatched the M16 from my hands, climbed the sand wall, aimed at the Somali's head, and shot one bullet straight into his face.

– *This is your first and last warning,* barked Elie. *You're up to it or you're not! If you're not, go back to filling magazines! This is war, not jardin d'enfants, he said.* (This is not kindergarten).

Soon, everyone calmed down. The guys got me a 7-Up. Good thing too, because I was about to faint. Elie and Michel gave me a pep talk and cheered me up. I was committed, or about to be. It was a matter of time, and that time would come less than few hours later.

As we filled our magazines and wiped dirt off our guns, we could hear a loud spine-chilling *"Allah Akbar"*, God is great, in a strange accent. This is how both sides (Muslims and Christians) taunted and provoked each other. The Machiavellian wit of politicians was only matched by the fighters' ignorance. Politicians on both sides made the Lebanese believe that this was a holy war between Christians and Muslims, a war of religious survival.

What was strange and confusing for me, was that one of my best friends when I was growing up was Muslim. We never knew the difference! He was in a Catholic School going to church every morning with all of us. It was because of the bloody war that we started to realize how religion played a huge role.

I armed my M16, jumped up, and headed to one of the firing holes in the bunker. Elie and Michel followed suit, and each knelt in front of a hole. This time I didn't think twice. I aimed and shot, hitting a Somali in the throat. He fell and did not stand up again.

The fighting round lasted around an hour and a half. A few Somalis were killed, but thank God no one from our battalion was hurt.

Elie and Michel congratulated me and officially welcomed me into the battalion. I had earned my stripes. I fit in. I could do this. On the other hand, I was a criminal. I had just killed a man or few! I would never get into Heaven.

God would be angry with me for the rest of my life. He would punish me and make me pay one way or another. This was not how I envisioned my life.

I missed my Dad like never before. Flashbacks of the very few memories I had of my father rushed through my head. I remembered how he used to wake Eby and me up, every Wednesday, by tapping on the door frame with our weekly allowance, 50 piasters back then. It was now five years since our Dad passed away. And for five years, day after day, I have knelt every night before I go to sleep and prayed one "Hail Mary" and one "Our Father" and asked God and Jesus to bring Dad back. I have been doing so because on the day Father passed away, one of my aunts held my hands, stared into my eyes and told me that if I knelt on my knees and prayed every night with all the faith I have got, God would bring my Dad back. I believed her back then. Today, I believe in God. I have not missed kneeling and praying the "Hail Mary" and "Our Father" one single night since then.

I came home one afternoon in the summer of 1980. It was 4:00 p.m. and I was supposedly back from school – and back from spending a couple of nights studying at the home of my childhood friend Christian. I opened the door, stepped in, and dropped my backpack on the floor, the backpack Mom and Eby always thought contained my schoolbooks. In reality, I had not slept for 48 hours as I had been on the front fighting. It was one of the fiercest weeks of the war.

Eby was at work. He used to do two shifts – mornings as a Graphic Designer in a small advertising agency near home, and nights as an editor at a children's magazine in Sassine Square, Ashrafieh.

"Bonjour, Mamy!" I shouted, without even knowing if she was home, and rushed to the bathroom. I filled the bathtub and lied in it. I was exhausted, completely drained. Lying in the bathtub, I could barely move; my lack of sleep and the soothing hot water left me numb. I reflected on where my life had led me so far and realized the stark truth: my life had led me nowhere!

My body relaxed in the hot water. I didn't feel myself falling asleep. I couldn't remember the last time I felt that good.

Two years earlier, in June of 1978, I had been hit for the first time. I will never forget that day. I was 15 years old. This was back in the notorious *Baneyet el Baton*, with Assir firing RPGs from the third floor. Assir was his call sign. It meant "shorty." None of us knew his real name. Assir was the weirdest guy I fought with. He was short, almost a midget, and a little mentally challenged with traces of Down Syndrome, but he was the fiercest fighter we'd ever seen. The craziest assignments were always thrown at him, and he never questioned his orders.

The Palestinian soldiers, more than I could count or see, were positioned in a building across the street. Assir and I were stationed in a room, behind a window fortified with sandbags. An RPG-7 shell had already doubled the size of that window. The entire building, a future residential condominium was still under construction, an unpainted shell with no stucco. To shoot an RPG-7, we had to secure enough space around us, mostly behind the weapon. If we didn't allow at least 10 feet behind us, the heat from the rear of the weapon would ricochet back and hurt us. To make things more complicated a RPG's shooting sources are traceable, and so once fired the enemy can easily locate where the shooter is hiding. Assir and I did not have adequate cover.

It was a good day by war standards. I was the shooter and Assir the re-loader. After shooting three rounds without attracting retaliatory fire, we prepared to climb down the building and join our battalion in the bunker. Assir gathered the remaining ammo and headed for the stairs first. I hung the RPG on my back and followed. I stood up and turned toward the stairs, my left side facing the window. This is when I felt a sting in my left knee. It felt like a wasp bite, a mild pain. I didn't bother to stop or look. I just rushed down the stairs to where Assir was waiting in the lobby. By now, my pain had intensified. I reached for my knee. It felt wet and warm. I looked at my bloody fingers. At the level of my knee, my khaki pants were saturated with blood. I tore away the mushy fabric and revealed my exposed flesh, a mix of tissue and blood.

– *Fuck! I've been shot! I'm hit!*

Assir did not even bother to turn around or see what I was talking about. He was really weird.

It was a sniper's M16 bullet. The .223 caliber bullet is notorious for its delayed effect. It is so thin and travels at such a high velocity that victims might not feel the pain until few seconds or more after they are hit.

By now, my pain was excruciating. I could barely stand. Assir and I started walking toward the bunker, but few feet later I fell. My shattered leg had failed me. Assir helped me stand up. I leaned on his shoulder, and we headed into the empty shipping container that served as our makeshift bunker. I expected to be triaged by whatever guys were in there, maybe someone would wrap a tourniquet around my leg and call in an ambulance.

To my good fortune Dr. Pierre Gedeon, a high-ranking officer and a physician, happened to be in the bunker. I would later find out he was there to consult with Elie, who was also a high-ranking officer, to discuss strategies for capturing an adjacent, well-positioned building on the border between East and West Beirut.

– I don't want to lose my leg. Please don't cut it off!

I collapsed into a chair and leaned back as Dr. Gedeon examined me. In my agony, he flexed my leg several times to confirm the integrity of my bones and kneecap.

– You're a lucky son of a bitch, Dr. Gedeon announced. *The bullet exited, and your knee bones were spared. Wrap him up,* he said to one of the other guys, *and take him to the hospital. Get a few stitches and you'll be ready to come back.*

Dr. Gedeon was unaware of the real reason behind my panic. He didn't know I was remembering my Dad's amputated leg. I knew how that looked. I knew what that could do to a man. I dreaded the idea of my mother going through the trauma once more of nursing an amputee. I remembered seeing pictures of Dad on the beach with his friends, always trying to hide the leg he did not have.

I recovered in a few days, and I even managed to keep my Mom and brother from knowing about the incident that could have blown my cover. They still had no idea that I was skipping school and was now a fighter. I said it was just a small accident, that I'd landed on some rocks jumping over a fence, and that I needed to stay home a few days.

Surprisingly, they fell for it. Had my older brother taken a similar path at this age he would surely have recognized the truth, but he had never taken up arms. At this time, Eby had two jobs and was still in school. My brother and I were like two roommates on opposite schedules. We shared a room, but we often went days without seeing each other. In the chaos of a civil war, your little brother can become a soldier and you might not even notice.

In September 1979, I was 16 and a half years old. Thirteen of my fellow fighters died in one afternoon, and 10 others were wounded. It all happened in Beirut's famous hotel area, in the Zaytouna district by the beautiful Mediterranean Sea. In addition to being a tall, attractive building facing the sea, the height of the approximately 25-story Holiday Inn was also strategically located. As we went about our business throughout Beirut, we were conditioned to see every building, every street, and every corner from a strategic point of view.

My battalion, along with two others, was on an offensive mission. We had orders to advance toward the hotel area, create a stronghold, and wait for backup.

After a long battle, backup came, but it was late. The three battalions gathered up and left the stronghold we had just established. We started the journey back through the narrow streets of Zaytouna, where most of the brothels were located before the war. Amazingly, some were still operational and catering to the fighters, me being one of them.

It was a hot and humid day in September 1979. While combing through the narrow streets of Zaytouna, we reached an exposed area that we had to cross. We had successfully navigated these streets before, but this time would be different. Snipers ambushed us instead of us ambushing them, all because we hadn't received backup in time. We were understaffed, and politics played a huge role. There must have been at least five or six snipers located in strategic areas overlooking the battalions' retreat route. Fighters fell like dominoes. There was nowhere to hide, and we were all running frantically to take cover wherever we could find it.

As I prepared to dive behind the wall of an old building, hollowed out by mortar shells, I was hit in the lower left side of my back. I fell and hit my head on a cinder block. I was in shock, but retained some measure of alertness. I remember Michel shouting over my head, calling me and asking me to stay with him. I kept thinking, *"Jamais deux sans trois"* (bad luck comes in threes). I knew I would survive this one, but I was convinced that the next time would be fatal.

I was taken to the hospital, where I thought of my Mom and brother. *"You're a lucky son of a bitch,"* the doctor said in English. That was the second time I heard that statement. He explained that it was a close call, and a miracle I could still walk. *"You could be laying there beside Elie, fighting for your life."* Elie had also been struck in the shoulder and lower back. His wounds were serious, much worse than mine, and he would remain hospitalized for a few months before returning to the fight.

I am a strong believer, and I had no doubt my escape from serious injury was indeed a miracle. I had never been so scared in my life. I had never felt so lonely, so confused, or so close to dying. I just wanted out.

I left the hospital that evening and stayed with my friend Christian. Back then, unless your injuries were significantly serious, you were immediately discharged from hospital. Christian wasn't fighting in the war, but he knew that I was – as did his father, a well-known doctor in the army. They both helped me keep my secret. When I returned home after being shot, I lied about my back pain, blaming it on more work-related accidents, lumbago, etc. They fell for it once more. They were starting to get used to my frequent absences. Staying away from home for 2 or 3 days was no longer something to worry about.

(Eby)
TO THE RED CROSS,
AND RECONCILIATION WITH LIFE
1981

Life went by. I am now working at an advertising agency in Badaro, close to the Green Line separating East Beirut from its West. It's a small agency but with clients that were fun to work for. One of them is White Horse Scotch Whiskey, so we were never short of brainstorming and creativity stimulant. There, I met the son of my godmother, Emilio. He works in the client-servicing department, another coincidence in my life full of strange occurrences.

Jad dropped out of school and has been working at our Uncle Joseph's clothing store, located on the upper side of Gemmayzeh, for two years now. Jad is a natural-born salesman, and he always had what it takes to communicate with people. School was not his thing, just as it was not for me. His charm and negotiation skills emerged at an early age. I could feel he is uncomfortable with the job; our uncle is bossy and borderline overbearing. Jad has a fully developed ego and strong personality. Obeying orders or being unjustifiably mistreated mark him for life. While most of his friends are still at school and on their Dad's payroll, he must cope at a young age with the harsh realities of life.

Before dropping out, I came to find out that Jad has not been attending school all the time. He was attending a *different school*, one that could have put an abrupt end to his dreams and his life, literally.

I returned home from work one day and walk into the main entrance just as Mom is trying to lift Jad's backpack lying on the floor by the umbrellas. It is so heavy that she drops it back.

– *Here, I'll help you with that.* I say while shutting the door.

– *My God Eby! Jad is killing me. Your brother has been bathing for almost an hour! Go see if he's OK*, she utters.

– *Hell no!* I reply. *You do it. I don't want to start another fight with him!*

– *Fine! God! I have to do everything around here.*

She rushes toward the bathroom, located at the end of the corridor, knocks and immediately opens the door sticking her head in. I am still standing at the other end of the long hallway. It is so foggy inside the bathroom that the steam gushes out, and I could barely see the bathtub from where I am standing.

– *Jad, are you OK? Jado?* No answer.

I was already in the bathroom when my mother calls my name.

– *Eby, come! Hurry!*

Jad is stretched out in the bathtub, fast asleep, with the top of his face sticking out of the foamy water. Mom, in panic, rushes toward him and starts shaking him vigorously. He opens his eyes startled, splashes water onto us and all over the floor.

– *Are you crazy?* Mom shouts. *You could have drowned? Holy Mary! You're going to give me a heart attack one day! Step out and dry yourself. Now! God!* And she leaves rushing towards the kitchen.

We have all our meals there, and occasionally take shelter during the heavy shelling in a small connecting room between the kitchen and the main corridor. It became Nadia's favorite place to sit, think, smoke, and drink coffee. I hear her light up a Kent.

Since Dad passed away, almost a decade ago, I developed a better understanding of our Mother's persona. Being more in a solitary state, and spending enough time at home, I get to witness Mom's daily living. Nadia's character comes to me as a revelation. Some might argue that I am still too young to delve into a Freudian analysis of her psyche; they are right. You see, this is not about psychology or analysis, but rather about the impact of Mom's sudden and salient presence in our lives.

When Dad was still around, Mom's role was more subdued, she simply was... Mom. Now, paradoxically enough, while trying her best to remain "Mom", and forced to simultaneously be a father, she is slowly losing her grip on both. As a mother whose spouse was in charge of everything, she is now required to learn the ropes of her new role. As a head of the family with two boys, filling the shoes of a father seems beyond her limits.

Mom in 1981 was a person that needed more help and attention than she, herself, can provide us. Constantly edgy and tense, she snaps for no reason. Her fear of losing her grip over us drives her into hysterical lapses. With a gentle and naturally obedient temper, instilled in her by a traditional Lebanese family where gender hierarchy is dominant, she finds herself struggling to impose her authority upon us. Add to that the absolute control of our uncles over our lives, and you end up with a kingdom where the queen is over-powered by the old guard.

Neither Jad nor I often ponder over how to make it easier on her; however, the rare awakenings we do have help in relieving some of the tension that would otherwise lead to disastrous consequences.

I am still standing in the bathroom, looking at Jad with a mixture of anger and regretful sadness.

– *What?* Jad asks.

I walk out and back to the main entrance at the other end of the corridor and sit by the phone on one of the wrought iron chairs. Every Lebanese house has a chair by the phone. Dialing out any number is a painstaking experience that requires patience and perseverance. We are lucky phone lines are still occasionally operational, with the war raging, telephone poles destroyed, and no maintenance. As I am vainly trying to call Aline, my girlfriend and wife-to-be, who lives just two blocks away, Jad shows up in his bathrobe, drying his hair with a towel. He nods. I give up on reaching Aline, hang up the phone and stare at him.

– *Jad, what in hell are you trying to do?*

– *What do you mean?* he replies with disdain as he walks toward the kitchen.

– *Wait! What are you doing to yourself, to Mom, to me, to us?*

He stops, turns and walks back toward me.

– *Nothing. I'm not trying to do anything. Why are you saying this?*

I keep staring at him while lifting the backpack that Mom could not carry, unzip it, reach in, and bring out an AK-47 with a foldable butt and place it on the floor. He looks at it for a while, and then stares at me. The look in his eyes slowly shifts from surprise, to anger, to perplexity. I pull out four magazines and two hand grenades. Jad told me later that every fighter was responsible for his weapons and ammunition and that they had to guard them with their lives. There is a long moment of silence. Our eyes are locked on each other's; only interrupted by Jad stealing a quick glimpse at the kitchen door, fearing Mom overheard our discussion.

– *We've already lost Dad. We can't take another loss,* I say while tears start forming at the corner of my eye.

Jad does not say a word. For the first time ever, he looks at me and seems to listen. Really listen. For once, I am speaking to my younger brother calmly and responsibly. For once, we are connecting.

From that moment on, our relationship started slowly shifting from one of two careless adolescents toward one of mutual respect. I always thought of Jad to be cold and hard, especially after Dad's death. He became distant, spending a lot of time out of the house without anyone knowing his whereabouts. We rarely talked, and when we did, we would fight. Don't get me wrong; I loved him more than anything in the world, but I felt as if we had nothing in common then, and I am sure he felt the same.

Now as I look back, I realize that we both had trouble understanding and accepting the divide between our diverging characters and the way we see things. Each of us is after his own ideals. My ideals are more utopic and emotional; while Jad's are more down to earth, more realistic. In a family without a father, amidst one of the bloodiest civil wars of the century, I have to admit that utopia is not the right way to go. The continuous career successes of Jad would prove that right.

I am still seated, looking at Jad, while he stares at the magazines in my hand. Without exchanging another word, Jad lowers his head and walks away. I return the magazines, rifle, and grenades into his backpack and carry it into our bedroom before Mom notices anything.

That night, as every night since Dad passed away, I prayed an "Our Father" and a "Hail Mary" before going to sleep. I found out a year later that Jad has been doing the same. I was shocked as we never talked about it. For me, that was an amazing moment, a kind of unspoken bond through prayer.

The next morning I am having my usual breakfast, biscuits dipped in a bowl of milk, while listening to the morning news on the radio giving an account of last night's mayhem, when Jad walks in still half asleep. He looks at me for a couple of seconds before greeting me with a mumble and walks toward the kitchen. He then stops and turns around.

– I'm going to headquarters today to hand over my badge and weapon. I'm quitting, he says.

Without waiting for an answer, he resumes his walk toward the kitchen and starts preparing his breakfast. Jad is an avid fan of Lebanese traditional food. His breakfast would consist of *"Labneh"* (Traditional sour cream similar to cheese) spread on a pita bread and garnished with olive oil, tomato, olives, fresh mint leaves, salt, and onions.

I don't say a word either, but deep inside of me I am so happy I can cry. I finish my breakfast with a shy smile.

That evening, Jad returns home late, goes straight to our bedroom and shuts the door. I follow him immediately. I am already thinking to myself that if we connected yesterday, I hope and pray that connection remains. I open gently the room door. Jad is sitting on his bed removing and flicking through items in his military duffle bag.

– *What happened? Did you quit?* I ask.

– *Oh! I fucking quit indeed!* He replied with an ironic tone.

– *You don't sound like you did. What happened?*

– *I told you I quit, and I did. It was not easy. They threatened me. They said that leaving the party is not an option. They see it more like desertion. I did not think I'd make it. But I managed to talk my way through.*

– *Really? How? What did you tell them?*

– *I mentioned Dad, Mom being alone, and how she can't afford to lose a son. Frankly. I don't know how they bought that shit! I finally told them that I decided to join the Red Cross instead. It's still a way to contribute to the civil war.*

– *And they fell for it?* I say surprised.

– *Yeah, they did... Well in a way, it is true.*

– *What is true?*

– *I am joining the Red Cross.*

Jad keeps his word and becomes a Red Cross first-responder. It is October 1981. I follow suit two months later.

After an intensive one-month training regimen, I graduate as a certified Lebanese Red Cross volunteer first-responder and join the Ashrafieh Station, one of the most active Centers in Lebanon, based in Gemmayzeh, number 102.

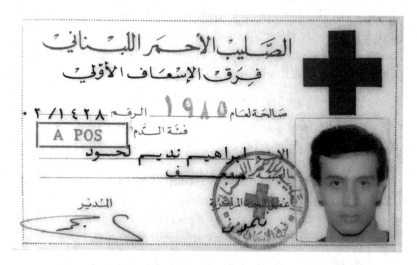

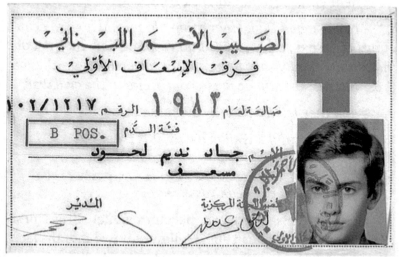

Our official red cross id cards. They were issued less than a year after we joined.

(Eby)
102
1982

It's a picnic, a fun ride. The first shift at 102 is a party! Most of us new recruits knew each other well. We all live in and around the neighborhood, went to the same school, and were in the same Scout packs for years. Most of us also go out together to the movies, the beach, gatherings, and New Year Eves.

Ego and pride are rocketing sky high. We feel like an untouchable elite. We are eagerly waiting for the first mission, the first time we will parade in the streets, taunting people in an ambulance with a large Red Cross on our chest and back. There are, of course, the few boys who anticipate giving their first CPR to a beautiful gal.

Jad, call sign Stanley, is not yet 18 years old, but through our cousin Jihad, who was already in the Red Cross, manages to get accepted. Jad is assigned to Team 5, where he finds himself with Jihad's brother, call sign Joura. Jad is the favorite among his team. He is witty, outspoken, and a rebel – unlike me. I am more of an introvert, a solo. So Jad is the popular guy and I am a sidekick. Quite funny when I think that, years earlier, it was the other way around. Before Dad passed away, Jad was the sweet tender cuddly boy with beautiful blond hair, while I (four years older) was reaching my teens with the agonizingly atrocious facial hair and acne.

I am assigned to Team 1 and choose Spirou as my call sign. It is the name of one of my favorite French comics characters. I am thrilled to find out that one of my best friends, call sign Boss, is also in my team. With us are also Mama, Eiffel, Shorty, Kebbeh, Nounours, Sierra, Skinny, and Souvlaki, a Lebanese of Greek origin who also managed to join the Red Cross while still 17 years old. His sister is the instructor who coaches the newcomers, including Jad and me. That's how things go around here in Lebanon – it's all about connections. We even have a specific word for it, "*Wasta*". You get by through the well-connected people you know; in Lebanon, everyone knows "someone".

It feels a bit awkward for us newcomers. Some fit, while others don't. Eiffel comes across snobbish, which makes the rest of the team wonder at what brought him to the Red Cross. No one will forget the first day he showed up. He was well-groomed and dressed, and had packed his own bed sheets, pajama, slippers, and sleeping pillow. He looked like a guy headed for a summer camp. When he saw the rest of the team, he just stood there perplexed and in apparent shock. A bunch of crazy guys swearing, cursing, belching, farting, and laughing. Everyone remembers how Eiffel pledged this to be his first and last shift with Team 1. He was determined to ask for a transfer.

As of the second shift, Eiffel becomes a full Team 1 member. For some reason, he integrates and is accepted by the rest of the pack. He would not give up his place to anyone, at any cost, and the rest of the team would not give him up either. Of course, he had to lose the pajamas and fancy bed sheets. A few weeks later, we find out that he has frequent heartburn. With his typical French accent he tells Boss, "Boss, *j'ai des aigreurs*." (French for "I have heartburns"). That sentence becomes the perfect description of Eiffel and spreads across 102.

We are each handed a white bib with a big red cross on the front and back. We also have at our disposal basic white plastic or metal helmets with the Red Cross sign on either side. They provide little head protection, but the color helps differentiate us from fighters and will, hopefully, spare our life. The orange official uniforms and berets came a year later. Bulletproof vests would be introduced after I left the Red Cross. We are also given a letter, called a "Mission Order", signed by the head of official Lebanese Red Cross Committee. For the first month or so, this paper will constitute the only evidence that we are Lebanese Red Cross first-responders. The round clip-on badges and identity cards carrying our photo, name, and serial number will come with the uniform. Four years later, my serial number "1428/102" would save my life.

Shifts are well orchestrated; from 6:00 a.m. to 6:00 p.m., and 6:00 p.m. to 6:00 a.m., which accommodates most of the volunteers who worked, went to school, or both. But when battles rage, no one goes to university or work, and 102 buzzes with action day and night. Night shifts are the busiest. Each of the five teams has already established its own routine, and that included checking the ambulances and supplies, assigning radio shifts, and preparing dinner.

During heavy fighting, night shift teams would join the day shifts and continue the missions they had already started. Similarly, the day shift team would sometimes stay and spend the night at 102 to help with the uninterrupted influx of missions. While we are busy saving lives, we all have loved ones we could never save from the torment of worry. The average age at 102 is 22 years of age. Most of us have parents who live for one purpose – to see their children grow up. During a civil war, this is a gift, a miracle by itself. Parents of volunteers live in constant worry and fear, and they have all the reasons to do so. Sadly enough, time would prove it right.

(Eby)
NO MORE SUICIDE MISSIONS FOR ME
1982

I rush down the stairs and out of the 102 Red Cross Center, run along the sidewalk, and reach the building entrance just one block away. I step in panting and out of breath. Bending over with my hands on my knees and breathing heavily, I thought that I seriously should stop smoking. I started when I was 15 with a pipe. I liked the smell of the tobacco and the intellectual look. But then came the macho guys at school and the neighborhood. They were all smokers, and what a better way to fit in than smoking myself? One cigarette led to the other, and in no time I was doing two packs a day. I've done it all, French *"Gitanes"*, Lucky Strike, Winston, and finally I became a red Marlboro addict. Some nights the coughing and chest pain became so unbearable that I would decide to quit cold turkey the very next day. But come morning, nothing helped me forget the past night like my first cigarette of the day.

I scan the building lobby to locate the stairs, and speed up to the second floor where one of the two apartment doors is ajar. I stand there for a few seconds, holding onto the cold forged-iron rail and trying to breathe normally. At 22, with my smoking habit, I had the lungs of a 40-year-old man.

There's an eerie silence and a smell of old damp stone. Suddenly, I'm startled by an old woman standing there silently, with a sad face and a void in her eyes. She must be the one who called 102. She points at the open door.

I walk toward the faint beam of light escaping from the half-open door, keeping an eye on the woman, and step in. Everything is tidy and calm in the austere apartment that is filled with typical 1960s furniture – vintage dark brown fabric couches and round coffee tables adorned with white crochet lace. On the center table, there is a plate with a variety of cigarette packs, which is part of a Lebanese custom of offering guests cigarettes with their Turkish coffee as a sign of hospitality. In one corner near a window, a tropical plant with large leaves is absorbing the morning sun. Light grey walls are scattered with cheap replicas of famous paintings. To my right, sits a large credenza, an entertainment system from the early 1950s with a turntable and a radio. Toward the end of the apartment, the dining room is as austere as everything else. On its wall hangs a big sepia photo of an old man. Afternoon shadows stretch through the lace curtains and on the intricate floor tiles. This was just another typical vintage Beirut home.

I scan the many doors exiting the living room. Only one is open wide. I tiptoe slowly toward it, as if to avoid waking up someone, and stick my head in first.

It is a large bedroom with lace curtains, a bed to the left, a large wardrobe to my right, and a dressing table facing me. The minimalistic decor gives a surreal dimension to the room.

A woman is lying peacefully on the bed, on her back, her left arm extended all the way and hangs over the edge of the bed. She is wearing a light blue nightgown and she seems asleep. I get closer, bend over, and notice her eyes are slightly open with tears running down her temples. She is staring at the ceiling as if waiting for an answer to a question she just asked. Her face is pale, very pale, and a dark shadow surrounds her eyes. On the bed table next to her is an empty jar of Valium.

Ten minutes earlier, 102 received the phone call. An old woman told them that she thought her neighbor is committing suicide. When prompted for details, she explained she had prepared a pot of coffee and came knocking on her neighbor's door for their ritual morning "*sobhieh*" (traditional morning gathering). When no one answered, she got worried and used the spare key the neighbor gave her years ago. When she found the poor woman lying motionless in bed, she rushed and called the Red Cross.

It is a Friday early morning. I was getting ready to head back home and then to work after my Thursday night shift.

I keep looking at the woman, trying to think of my next action. I pull my radio from the left leg pocket of my orange overalls. I page 102:

– *102, 102, Spirou.*

– *Spirou, 102.* It is Boss on the other side of my radio.

– *I have a suicide attempt, one block down from the Center. Same building as Momo's father's shop, second floor. Send an ambulance and team immediately.* Momo is another first-responder at 102.

I place the radio on the bedside table and sit next to her, gently pull her hanging arm onto the bed, and hold her hand.

– *Help is on the way. You're young and beautiful. Why?*

– *I can't take it anymore. It has to end. Please let it end. Leave me alone. I don't want help.*

Tears keep falling down her temples, disappearing between her light brown hair, sprinkled with a few grey strands.

– The ambulance is on its way. You're gonna be fine. Stay with me. Do not close your eyes. Talk to me.

I find myself trying to hold my own tears back. I don't know why. I move my head away and stare at the window. Maybe the light pouring in could bring with it some hope. I look around, trying to find a photo or something to identify the cause of this situation. A radio is playing somewhere, actually two radios. One is delivering the news (and you could recognize Sharif Al Akhaoui's voice giving a rundown of the situation at the front) while another set is playing Wadih El Safi's *"Lebnan ya ot'et Sama"* (Lebanon, a Piece of the Heaven).

For a minute, I see myself sitting on the bed, next to my father, trying to wake him up. That was exactly 10 years ago. Suddenly, I am 12 years old again.

I turn my head back and look at the woman. Her eyes are closed. Panicking, I grab her by the shoulders and shake her. *"Stay with me, stay with me! What's your name?"* Something inside of me is screaming, *"Don't let your Dad die again!"*

She opens her eyes slightly, looks at me a while, turns her head away and with a faint and barely audible voice, she says "Amal."

I smile.

– Amal, you know what your name means, right? (It means hope in Arabic.) *You have to live up to your name, Amal.*

– *I can't take it anymore. He left me. I am alone. I can't take care of my kids. Let me go.*

As I pray for the guys to arrive fast, Boss and Mama step in the room with a stretcher.

Amal is finally rushed down the stairs, into the ambulance, and straight to the St. George Hospital. The roads are empty and it only takes 5 minutes to get there.

Amal's stomach is drained and her life is saved. Saved, but for what? She had no one to come back to.

We head back to 102. There, I immediately go to the radio room, tell the first-responder there that I will take over his shift, and sit alone panting. I will not go to work, not for now at least. How many times did I think of killing myself? How many times did I watch Mom getting that close to committing suicide? Our father had left too, 10 years ago. After that, life became a roller coaster for Jad and me. I could handle anything, but not suicide missions. Not anymore.

The "smurfs" of team 1 posing for an "unusual" photo to say the least!
I'm squeezed right in the middle.

(Eby)
THE "SANAFER"
1982

After dozens of shifts and bonding, we decided it was time to brand Team 1. To us, it is similar to creating a sorority, a pact for life in times of death. We watch each others' backs and become a family. Most of us were boy scouts and used to the concept of packs rather than teams – just like wolves – and to having totem names. As a matter of fact, when I was a boy scout, I was in the Wolves pack.

That day, while having dinner, I jump frantically and shout:

– *From now on, we will be the "Sanafer"* (Arabic plural for Smurfs). *Each one of us will have a "Sanfour" title.*

The *"Schtroumpfs"* (Smurfs in French), a popular French Belgian comics series by famous cartoonist Peyo, is widely read and loved in Lebanon. A year later, a small fast food restaurant opened with the same name. Copyright laws were never one of our government's forte, let alone during a civil war.

And so we had a name. Now there is *"Mama Sanfour"* (Mama), *"Baba Sanfour"* (Boss), *"Teta Sanfour"* (Skinny), and so on. I am bestowed the *"Sanfour Sex"* title, because of my foul language and constant sexual innuendos. The news spread all over 102, and beyond to some of the other Centers around the country.

A few months later, Team 5 decides to follow suit and become the *"Sanejib"* (Arabic for squirrels). There's always an underlying but friendly competition between the two teams in 102; but when it comes to duty, the Squirrels and the Smurfs constitute a fabulous team. Jad is in Team 5, which we all consider the macho team.

For us, the Smurfs team constitutes a means of venting. Remember, we are all aged between 18 and 25. Rather than living like most young men of our age around the world, we are stuck in the maelstrom of a civil war, punctuated by daily deprivation and death.

As a young man – and to this very day – I was a very sensitive person. Although quite rational and methodic, most of what I do is ruled by the emotional consequences of my actions. I have trouble understanding the behavior of macho men, yet I want to belong to their pack. That paradox is a result of the isolation imposed on me after Dad's demise and the solitude I willingly forced myself into. Just like the Red Cross, the Smurfs emphasize my will to reconcile with the rest of the world, my way of joining a pack.

It was very late, around 1 or 2 am. We couldn't sleep, so we decide to goofing around! Few minutes later we were called for a mission.

(Eby)
THE SPARE TIME OF MISFITS
1982

By unanimous consent, Team 1 consists of mostly "crazy" people. Two routines are immediately established: eating five-star food and watching movies that had to contain at least one erotic moment. Mind you, there was nothing "obscene" or pornographic about it, but just enough to stir a laugh or two. No one agrees exactly on how it all started; all I recall is Souvlaki becoming the official provider of movies. He would show up at every shift carrying new videotapes. At 102, there is an old VHS video tape player attached to an even older TV with no remote control. Someone actually has to walk over to the set to change channels or fix the constantly flickering image. After dinner, we all gather on the large sofa, huddle against each other like penguins in the Arctic winter, and pop in the movie.

Watching the guys monkey around and utter crude remarks every time a daring shot appears is by far more interesting than watching the movie. The boys make jokes about the movie's storyline, actors, and cheesy plots... and the girls? Well, they mostly complain about the funky furniture, old-fashioned hairdos, and other production details.

The girls of the Lebanese Red Cross in general, and those of 102 in particular, are some of the coolest people you would ever meet. Totally at ease with themselves and among young men with hormones surges, they blend in perfectly and impose a positive influence on the mood, the missions, and the Center's daily operations. Many close mixed-gender relationships developed; some did not go far, while some ended happily for ever after. One of those relationships ended so abruptly it brought 102 to its knees.

At Team 1 we're blessed with some of the coolest girls of 102, but one of them stands out and shines. Mama is revered by all the team members. Constantly clear-headed and pragmatic, she masters the art of achieving missions with such grace and class. Nothing stops Mama.

On a Thursday night shift, a lull reigns on the war fronts and we are watching an action movie from the early 70s. As we reach a scene where the hero grabs the girl, kisses her, and throws her on the bed in a cheap motel, Mama (rational and calm as always) is watching silently when she suddenly rises and solemnly shouts, *"Come on guys! We've seen this one already!"*

While the hardy girls in my team have trouble covering their embarrassment, Skinny throws another movie on. *"Yuck! The curtains in that motel suck. Look at the colors. And that furniture is totally tasteless!"* Both remarks become classics at 102.

The next shift, Souvlaki arrives late with a new tape. Boss, now Team 1 leader, starts reprimanding him. Souvlaki argues that the tape he holds is the best of the best, an "Oscar Winner" according to him. While the rest of team is lying on the only sofa in the huge living area digesting dinner, he pops the tape into the VCR, clicks on "play", and in one leap falls on the sofa between Skinny and me.

As the tape starts, everyone finally understands how twisted Souvlaki is. He has spent hours working with the video shop owner, editing scenes from different movies and overlaying them with popular Arabic songs that hilariously depict or describe the scenes. That night, we received phone calls from the neighbors asking us to lower our voices... and the music. The funny part is that we were silent.

It is still 1982, and later that year the infamous Ashrafieh battle breaks out. Shelling grows so intense that some areas of the living quarters of 102 became hazardous. We agree to move the living room to the narrow corridor linking the living-dining area with the bedrooms and toilets.

102 is located on the second floor of an old Lebanese house with high ceilings, large rooms, and a central corridor that is about 5 feet wide and 25 feet long. We stack mattresses and pillows at one end, and our precious TV and VCR at the other.

Every time we get a break, we gather in the corridor that now looked like an Ottoman *"diwan"* (an Arabic-style seating area with cushions spread on the floor that is inherited from the Ottoman/Turkish culture) and watch movies. Fearing prying eyes, we develop a synchronized drill. In case anyone unexpectedly shows up while we are watching our movies, we practiced removing the tape and replacing it with *Gone with the Wind* in less than 5 seconds. And it worked. One of us hits the "eject" button, one removes the tape, a third pops in the alternate tape, and the one who clicked "eject" hits "play". Perfect orchestration.

One afternoon, despite the heavy shelling, the radio is silent. The morning was very busy. We carried out many missions in and around the Ashrafieh sector. We had just finished a quick lunch and were relaxing in the makeshift living room. An old Feyrouz theater play was airing on LBC, the Christian Forces TV channel. Souvlaki, apparently bored with the "lesser educational" nature of the broadcast, goes to the sleeping quarters and returns with one of "his" movies. Without asking anyone's permission, he slides the tape in the VCR. Another completely tasteless Western-Italian is now unfolding. For once, everyone is happy about the deafening sound of the shelling. It covers the movie's out of sync soundtrack.

We stay there, lying about and uttering some lame joke from time to time. Only Souvlaki is watching with intense fervor. He even waves his arm at us, asking us to shut up, as if missing the dialog would ruin the whole plot. He gets frantic when another kissing and foreplay scene is on screen, begging us to watch.

Shorty is manning the radio shift. He suddenly rushes in.

– Guys he's here! Number 2 is here!

Number 2 is the second in command at the Red Cross and a big fan of 102, which he visits frequently. He must have been in the neighborhood, or on his way back from headquarters. Either way, time has come to put the 5-second drill to test. It works perfectly, and by the time the three tape-swapping kamikazes had loaded *Gone with the Wind* into the VCR; Number 2 is at the corridor entrance.

He looks at the TV screen and screams with delight

– No way! You're watching Gone with the Wind? This is my favorite movie.

Long story short, it was the most boring afternoon in 102's Team 1 annals. We watched *Gone with the Wind*, all 3 hours and 58 minutes of it, including the end credits. Afterward, we agreed to keep a copy of *Jaws* beside the VCR.

During one of the many drills conducted to stay in shape. Here Jad can be seen (third from the right), and me from the back kneeling in the foreground.

(Eby)
OF DELTA, SLEEPING BEAUTIES
AND BOMB SHELLS
1982

Delta is the unwanted twin of 102. It had to be created because of the intense battles plaguing Ashrafieh in the spring and summer of 1982. Shelling became so intense that 102 had to be split in half. Ashrafieh is the heart of the Christian Beirut. Situated on a hill that culminates on Sassine Square, it is the epitome of the cross-classes fusion. It's home to both the wealthy families of Beirut as well as the working middle class. Ashrafieh's streets are mostly narrow and winding. They feel warm and cozy, and are lined with sycamore trees, small grocery and clothing shops, and restaurants that serve everything from falafel to Italian. Most buildings of Ashrafieh date back to the 1960s and older. Vintage Lebanese houses with red tiled roofs and small gardens laced with forged iron fences blend with modern buildings in an oddly harmonious way.

There, in the heart of Ashrafieh, on a parallel road to the famous Sassine Square, is the school of the Lazarists monks.

It is July of 1982, and schools are on summer break. The Lazarists management agrees to offer us a large underground storage hall that is also equipped with bathrooms. The 102 twin is born, code name "Delta". Its sole purpose is to serve the upper Ashrafieh area and adjacent neighborhoods, while 102's main Center would remain in charge of downtown East Beirut and Gemmayzeh. My team was one of those assigned to Delta while others remained at 102. The heavy shelling made it hazardous for us to drive all the way to Gemmayzeh, so I could see neither Jad nor Mom anymore. This situation went on for months. Fortunately, Jad could still check on Mom from time to time.

My life is full of coincidence. Remember the band I told you about few chapters ago? Sirocco? Remember where our rehearsal basement was located? It was at the Lazarists Monks School, and today, I'm back there once more! This time me and the country are singing a different tune. My band is 102 and the music playing is the drums of war.

When we have to drive to 102, it is for the sole purpose of transporting supplies or blood from the blood bank. Trips are short, hazardous, and swift. These are the only times I could see Jad, if I am lucky enough to find him there and not out on a mission. Aside from those occasional reciprocal visits, our only link with 102 is through the radio.

Delta is located right under the main recess court of the convent-school and is accessible through one long and straight flight of stairs. The ambulances are parked in the middle of the court. We managed to split the underground hall into multiple virtual service areas. There are the radio and equipment quarters, the kitchenette, dining and common areas, and the sleeping corner located at the far end of the long corridor. But no matter how hard we try, it still feels like a giant underground hall.

Life at Delta is hectic. Missions are frequent and the streets of Ashrafieh are treacherous. If you have not been through a civil war, and I hope you never do, it will be hard to grasp the breadth and width of the tragedy. Lebanese people are happy, outgoing, and fun, and "westernized" in mentality and behavior. The majority is educated and speak three languages fluently. All this to state that war is not embedded in our culture; 6 years later the Lebanese Civil War still takes its toll on the spirit and resolve of the Ashrafieh population. Each of its inhabitants has lost loved ones to the war. Some lost their business or home. Some lost their will to resist and live. If you think it is easy to spend the night crouching in the corner of a bedroom or cramped in a bathroom because it is the safest place in the house, think again. The fear and trauma that accompany the whistle of a mortar flying over your head is indescribable. Trust me, I know. I spent endless nights with my Mom and Jad lying on the floor in a corner of our bedroom. With every whistle, you wait for the mortar to fall and blow up inside the room. First, the utter silence between the whistles, the wait, the suspense, and the heart-stopping anguish. Then comes the deafening detonation, followed by the sound of falling rubble, broken glass, and sometimes the cries and wails of the injured. The stench of gunpowder fills the air. The irony is that you are happy you're still alive, that it was not you – it was someone else. Back then I was 15 and Jad was 12. This is how we both grew up. This is how Ashrafieh and the rest of the country's children and teens grew up.

Driving through the narrow streets of Ashrafieh, one of the oldest neighborhoods of Beirut, is painstakingly hard. Its streets are seldom straight or wide. Cars parked on both sides of the road leave a narrow lane for circulation, let alone fallen debris and mortar craters. The missions at Delta, aside from the usual, have a new factor injected: psychological trauma. In many cases, 102 is called upon to transport young men and women in near-coma states because of fear induced by their homes and neighborhoods being subjected to heavy shelling. 102 volunteers are more emotionally affected by these missions than by the dead and wounded. The memory of *Amal*, the suicide patient haunts me every time I see men and women in shock.

It is a Thursday evening in early June 1982 in Beirut. The weather is mild, the days are long, and the nights are very pleasant. It is not yet hot and humid, and we can maneuver more easily without the winter outfits or the summer sweat.

The week has witnessed some of the heaviest shelling since the start of the so-dubbed "Ashrafieh battle". It is so heavy that on some occurrences, 102 is strictly forbidden from conducting any missions in until the shelling winds down. Putting the lives of both the victim and the volunteers at risk would not help much.

At 6:05 p.m. the order is sent for an ambulance to rush to a street near Sassine Square, less than half a mile from Delta. A girl in a traumatic state of shock is the only information given by Operations, which received the quick phone call from one of the girl's relatives.

Boss and I are in the yard, running the evening routine ambulances checklist. Mama and Eiffel come up running and inform us of the mission and jump inside the ambulance that is being checked. Boss shouts:

– *No, not the 177! It's not fully checked yet. We'll take the 178.*

Boss is very picky and hates to go on a mission and later find out that we're missing an item in the ambulance inventory.

Mama and Eiffel jump out of the 177 ambulance and into the 178, where she sits in the back while Eiffel takes the wheel. He and few others are certified ambulance drivers. Boss takes the front seat. I close and lock the doors of the 177 and hop in the back with Mama.

We reach a narrow street in the neighborhood that is packed with buildings proudly protruding their large balconies laced with beautifully ornate cast iron rails and stone or light yellow-colored facades. The ambulance stops in front of the presumed location. Eiffel reverses the ambulance onto the sidewalk and parks it almost perpendicular to the street between two cars. It is the only available spot and there's no time to look for another one. It also makes it easier to reach the entrance and take shelter in case the shelling gets stronger.

As per protocol, the ambulance driver stays with the

ambulance while the three other first-responders head for the casualty. The building's forged steel and glass door opens. Most of the glass has disappeared, and shards could still be seen on the floor. A shell must have fallen nearby recently. A middle-aged man waves at the team and says:

– *She's downstairs, in the shelter. We're there since yesterday morning. Follow me.*

The shelling is gradually intensifying and we can hear the chilling sound of the mortars' whistles as they whizz over our heads. This is not a good sign.

– *Spirou, follow the guy. Mama and I will get the stretcher,* orders Boss.

The shelter is located one floor below the ground level. Narrow stairs lead down to a small area with two metal doors. The heavy smell of fuel indicates that one of the doors lead to the central heating burners. The other door is ajar, and a shy beam of dancing light sneaks out – candles. The electric current has been out for the past 48 hours. At Delta, we're surviving on a generator that feeds the radio and basic amenities.

– *Over here,* says the man, *please, please, go in.*

I push the door and step in ahead of the man. It's a relatively small space, not more than 15 by 15 feet, packed with people, bunk beds, blankets, bottles of water, few suitcases, and black trash bags. In a corner, someone had brought a portable camping gas stove on which a teakettle is still sitting. There is also another camping gas lamp hanging on the wall. It is off; they probably ran out of gas canisters.

To my left, on one of the bunk beds, a young woman is lying on her back, neatly covered with a blanket. She seems to be sleeping peacefully, but everyone is staring at her anxiously. I guess she is the one.

I kneel next to her. Her mother is sitting on an empty can of "Nido" powdered milk, silently crying and caressing her hair.

– *Can you please give us some space?* I ask gently but authoritatively.

The man that led me to the shelter starts gently nudging and pushing the curious onlookers who try to squeeze themselves on the other side of the shelter. The mother stands up, pushes her makeshift seat under the bunk bed and stands next to the wall, above the victim's head.

– *She was so scared. She's always been afraid of the bombs. Yesterday was insane. The poor thing could not take it. She was hysterical, crying all night.*

I check the girl's vital signs while listening to the mother. Her pulse is weak and her breathing slow. She is almost white, and small beads of sweat are forming on her forehead. I try to wake her up by gently tapping on her cheeks.

– *What's her name?* I ask the man, who I realize is her father.

– *Lina.*

I look up at the mother and ask:

– *And she's been like that since when?*

– *Almost an hour and a half. We tried to wake her up. We sprinkled rose water on her face... I beg you, do something. She is 18 years old... only 18.*

Boss and Mama enter the room at that moment with the stretcher and oxygen.

– *Don't worry*, I say to the mother in an unconvincing tone, *she will be fine.*

While Mama and I prep the stretcher, Boss places the oxygen mask on the girl's face, calibrates the intake, and removes the blanket off her, ready to move her to the stretcher.

Her mom is crying loudly now, and neighbors try to console her.

– *I want to go with her,* she shouts.

– *Are you crazy?* replies the husband, *can't you hear what's going on outside? No one moves. I'm going.*

Boss and I carry the girl onto the stretcher while Mama watches for her head and oxygen mask. We lift the stretcher and start the ascent to the building entrance. Beirut buildings are always a challenge to stretcher-bearers. Stairs are narrow and with sharp angles. Stretchers have to be tilted in all directions and often to dangerous angles. Patients are firmly strapped to prevent them from falling off.

We reach the ground floor right when a mortar shell falls close, very close; so close that the remaining pieces of glass hanging to the putty on the forged steel gate come flying into the building lobby where we were standing with the stretcher. As a reflex, we fall back a few steps down the stairs.

– *Eiffel! Are you ok?* shouts Boss immediately.

– *Yeah, yeah. I'm fine,* answers Eiffel with his typical nonchalant voice.

He pops his head through the gate and smiles awkwardly while holding his helmet with one hand and a cigarette in the other. Eiffel is also a heavy smoker.

– *Get your ass in here now,* barks Boss as the smoke and gunpowder smell from the nearby explosion reach us, *and put your bloody helmet on!*

We wait for a few minutes, just in case a follow-up shell falls, which is typical. Nothing comes. We rush with the stretcher to the ambulance. Eiffel has already opened both the back and side doors.

We help each other slide the stretcher into the ambulance. The victim's Dad climbs in and sits facing his daughter. Mama follows. Boss sits in the front. I am still standing to the left side of the back door. I fold the tray and then the flap. Before climbing in, I instinctively throw a look at the sidewalk toward the building's gate to see if anyone is still standing there. As I look in the opposite direction, the front of the ambulance is in sight. This is when I notice…

Eiffel starts the ambulance and gets ready to turn the front wheels to exit the sidewalk. I shout from the bottom of my lungs:

– *Eiffel! Stop! Stop!*

Eiffel hits the breaks, and Boss pops his head out of right window.

– *What? What is it?*

– *There's a shell under your tire. There's an unexploded shell!*

A 60-caliber mortar shell is half embedded in the

asphalt right under the right front tire of the ambulance. Had he moved up one inch, Eiffel would have driven over and probably triggered it. He pulls the hand break and shuts the engine. Boss opens the door to step down.

– *No! Don't come down, not from this side,* I shout.

– *Nobody moves,* yells Boss as he shuts his door. *Eiffel, let's step out from your side.*

I show Boss the location of the shell. The tire is almost leaning on it. We carefully give instructions to Eiffel to drive backward as far as the ambulance goes, then steer completely in the opposite direction and slowly move forward.

The maneuver takes 5 grueling minutes while Mama and the victim's father are sitting in the ambulance impatiently. We finally manage to move the ambulance away from the shell and drive to the hospital. The shelling is starting to intensify alarmingly, so much so that we completely forgot to inform anyone about the dangerous shell embedded in the pavement.

To make things worse, the only available hospital is in Baabda, another 12-mile drive and on a hazardous road. Baabda is where the Presidential Palace and the Ministry of Defense are located; not the kind of place one would want to go to in such situations. The road is sprinkled with checkpoints of the different warring factions, and some of the streets leading there are notorious for being prime targets and dangerously exposed to sniper attacks.

Once there, we carry the victim, still in a coma, to Emergency, and then into a room on the upper floors, and leave. Eiffel has found the time to light up a cigarette while parked in front of the Emergency access. Both Boss and I join in.

– *Don't you think we should have unloaded the patient, her Father, and Mama during the maneuver back there?* I whisper to Boss.

During the civil war, as in any war, there are occasional brief lulls. Shelling winds down and all we can hear are sporadic sniper gunshots, so we come up from Delta's underground to the courtyard, bask in the sun, or clean the ambulances stained with blood and dirt from the previous day's missions. We also run the ambulance checklist and refurbish the stocks. This is a mandatory routine for 102's Team 1. It was both Boss and my original idea. The day I joined, Boss and I decided to make sure the ambulances are in perfect shape and fully equipped before the start of every shift. So, I brought some graph paper from home and traced on every sheet an elaborate checklist of all the items in the ambulance stock. At the start of every shift, we toured the entire Center's ambulances, checked the supplies, and marked the missing items. We then refurbished the ambulances from the Center's stock room. The checklist later became mandatory at 102 and throughout the Lebanese Red Cross. Of course, what started as my handwritten checklist is now an official printed form.

After a week of moving to Delta, things began getting rough. We would only leave the basement to go on critical missions or replenish life-sustaining supplies.

Food is scarce, and we have to do with whatever stocks we have; corned beef, processed cheese, and canned vegetables. Most of us lose weight due to the lack of healthy nourishment. We miss the gourmet dinners of the days at 102.

The ambulances of 102 and 101 headquarters in Spears, West Beirut, are always prone to theft. Militiamen would stop the ambulance at gunpoint, let the first-responders out, and just drive away with the vehicle, leaving the team on a sidewalk with no cover from the shelling, and sometimes no radio to call for help. Later, the ambulance would be found dumped in some street, blood dripping from the back and side doors, riddled with bullet holes, and medical equipment and stretchers missing.

We had to drive the ambulances back to Delta, wash them thoroughly, and try to restore them to working conditions. Ambulances 177, 178, and 180 were assigned to 102. It is hard to explain, but you end up developing some kind of a weird connection to these cars, as if they had a soul of their own. We know every detail about them by heart, including their glitches.

At night, between missions, we keep ourselves busy by practicing judo. Kebbeh is a fifth-Dan black belt, and he agrees to train us to stay fit. It brings back happy memories of my Dad registering me at my school's judo classes back in 1970. He would come watch me practice, although I must admit I was not really born for sports. I am more the intellectual kind of guy, and my physical talents are rather limited.

We thought Delta would last a couple of months and that we would all be back to 102 by summer's end. We were wrong. The Ashrafieh Battle was the focus of relentless Syrian shelling on the Christian district. It would last for another 6 months. Schools and universities remain shut.

Young students are ecstatic, while parents live through the nightmare of seeing their children missing another school year, and eventually their future. I remember how ecstatic I was at first when we started missing school days during the early years of the War, which started in 1975. We were just kids, oblivious of the future and careers. A day without school is a miracle, let alone whole weeks.

February 1983 came. It was Valentine's Day. Trying to make it a fun evening, we decided to kiss all the team's girls... on the lips. I kissed Josette whose call sign is *Souris* (French for mouse). Ironically, Josette, a member of my team, would become Jad's wife 2 years later. They were not yet in a relationship when we kissed. Of course, my brother found out later, and we still tease each other about it till this day.

(Jad)
SHEIKH BASHIR
1982

Tuesday, September 14, 1982.

It was not an ordinary day. It was supposed to be the turning point of the war. The entire month of September was extraordinary. Bashir Gemayel (commonly known as Sheikh Bashir, leader of the Lebanese Forces Christian militia, widely considered the savior, even by most of his foes, the man who would deliver Lebanon from the civil war) was elected President of the Lebanese Republic.

On that day, at 4:00 p.m., Sheikh Bashir arrived at the headquarters of his party in Sassine, Ashrafieh, to deliver a farewell speech to his comrades in arms and officially resign from the party to assume his duties as President of the Lebanese Republic. Half an hour later at 4:30 p.m. sharp, a briefcase packed with a 250-pound remote-controlled bomb, and strategically placed on the floor above, exploded and brought the whole building down, killing Sheikh Bashir and 11 others and wounding about 100 others.

102 immediately received the order to move to the bomb site. Eby was at home that day, working on a special project related to his work when he heard the news. Radio and TV stations were already broadcasting live from the scene and all claimed that Sheikh Bashir survived with only superficial wounds. Although deeply saddened by the news, the Lebanese were jubilant about the survival of

Sheikh Bashir, the President who would save the nation.

I was in the Kleiat mountain village, 25 miles from Beirut, spending the day at my best friend Christian's summer home. I had brought along a radio transmitter, something first-responders would do to stay in touch in case of emergency. This was years before cellphones would become commonplace. After the presidential elections, everyone was kept on standby. It was 4:35 p.m. We were parked near Christian's home; sitting in the old Dodge Coronet I had bought from my uncle while working for him, the very same car I used to spend most of my Saturday mornings washing and polishing while my friends would pass by on their way to the beach. Christian was in the front smoking a cigarette and listening to music, while I was in the back making out with my girlfriend Mireille. It may sound funny or even questionable why Christian was with me in the car while I was with Mireille. Although Christian and I were very close, obviously, I did not plan on making out with Mireille while he was with us in the car. We all went for a ride and an ice cream, and the moment presented itself... In fact, the presence of Christian with us in the car made it easy for Mireille and me to be together; if we were to be caught alone by the police, it would have been a disaster. It is against the law to get intimate in a car. The radio crackled:

– *Stanley, Stanley, 102.*

Startled, I pushed Mireille to the side and started looking around on the floor, trying to find the radio. For 102 to call me it had to be an emergency. We were not allowed to use the radio for any other means of casual communication.

– *Stanley, 102. Come in, Stanley.*

I dropped onto the floor of the car, squeezed myself between the front and back seats looking for the transmitter and shouting at Christian, *"Where's the fucking radio? Where did you put it?"*

– *Me? I did not touch your radio, man!*

– *Help me fucking find it!*

My buddy Christian and I had a peculiar relationship. We've been best friends since kindergarten. Between my strong, aggressive personality and Christian's tender almost docile temper, we were like fire and ice. But through some magical formula our relationship worked like clockwork. We were inseparable.

Mireille, buttoning up her shirt, suddenly said, *"Jad, there, under the passenger seat."*

I bent further and reached under the seat, grabbed the radio, pushed the talk button, and before I pulled my hand from underneath the seat, I shouted, *"102, 102, Stanley."*

– *Stanley, you are needed immediately at the Center. Huge explosion in Ashrafieh, at the President's headquarters.*

– *102, what? Bashir? Chocolat?*

– *Stanley, 102. No names! We don't know. Come now to 102.*

– *On my way!*

I drop the radio on the seat.

– *Christian, move away. Quick. Fuck. Fuck. Move away!*

Christian slid to the passenger seat; the car had a single long front seat. I jumped over behind the wheel, started the car, and took off in a cloud of burning rubber. I did not stop mumbling:

– Fuck, fuck. Bashir is dead, I can feel it. Fuck!

In the back seat, Mireille was crying and begging me to slow down. Christian looked numb, sinking into the passenger seat without a word. I dropped off both of them at Christian's home, swung the car around, and sped toward Beirut. At that time, it should take me around 45 minutes. I made it to 102 in less than 30 minutes, parked the car on Tabaris Square, and ran into the Center, where I was briefed. I got ready, grabbed the next ambulance, and left for the explosion site. Teams from 102 and other Centers were flocking to the site. Eby could not participate in this rescue because the Red Cross prohibits direct relatives from going on missions together, let alone brothers.

The devastation was horrible. The small three-story vintage building squeezed into a narrow street that led straight from Sassine Square was surrounded by other small houses and 1960s buildings. Ironically, in a building right behind the bomb site, lived our Mother's cousin and her family. They were miraculously spared.

The first-responders scoured the debris, searching for survivors and bodies. The three-story building had collapsed like a wafer. The dead and wounded were trapped mostly on the ground floor between the rubble and ceilings. To make things worse, collective hysteria prompted civilians, neighbors, bodyguards, and militiamen to search for the dead and wounded, which rendered the rescue efforts even harder to perform. While the Civil Defense tried to put out the fire, my colleagues and I searched for victims, provided first aid to the wounded, and transferred many to nearby hospitals. Rescue efforts continued well into the night. Rumors about Sheikh Bashir spread throughout Lebanon and the world. Some said he'd been seen walking out of the debris and giving the victory sign. Others claimed to see him being carried in the now infamous ambulance number 175. A few had already spread the news that he was found dead. None of this was true at that time.

I would later learn that Eby was at home during this time, anxiously waiting for news. In the early evening, he went to 102 to seek updates; no one knew anything yet about Sheikh Bashir. So, Eby walked back home, but not before vainly trying his luck one last time and asking if he could join the teams on site. He went to bed around midnight. Next to him, on my empty bed, he placed his Red Cross overalls and badge. He also kept beside him a radio that he picked from 102 to be contacted in case of emergency. During the civil war, telephones were unreliable. Eby was restless, but by 1:00 a.m., he managed to fall asleep. Not for long though. At 2:30 a.m. on September 15, Eby awoke to the screeching of his radio.

– *Spirou, Spirou, Stanley!*

It took him a while to wake up and grab the radio.

– *Stanley, Spirou. What's happening?*

– *If you see the site... Come out on the balcony. I'm down here, under the building.*

Eby jumped out of bed and rushed to the balcony, barefoot and naked except for his boxers. It was chilly and the balcony floor was cold. Eby wrapped his chest with his arms and looked over the balcony rail. I was standing next to an ambulance in full attire and helmet. We looked at each other in the dark of the night, each of us holding our radios.

– *Come up for a while,* said Eby.

– I can't. I have to go back. We just dropped off a Chocolat (deceased person) *at HDF* (Hôtel-Dieu de France Hospital)

– How is it going back there? It's bad, right?

– Yeah, very bad. I'll be back in few hours and tell you all about it.

I climbed back into the ambulance and rushed away in the empty, dimly lit street. For Eby, the night was over. He went to check on Mom, but she was already awake and reciting a rosary. Nadia seldom slept, and Eby had inherited his insomnia from her.

I returned home 24 hours later. I was not allowed to leave 102 before Sheikh Bashir's team, spoke with me and got a full description of what I saw and what I did. I was exhausted and my orange overalls were filthy and stained. My face and naked skin were coated in grey dust from the blast site. In our home, I sat on the dining room sofa and gave Eby and my Mom an empty stare.

– I found him. I found him! Damn! He's dead!

Mom switched on the small Panasonic transistor radio. The morning news bulletin on Voice of Lebanon was just starting. There was no mention of Sheikh Bashir's death. The news anchor stated that Sheikh Bashir was in the hospital and more news would be provided soon. Eby, Mom, and I were among the very few who knew the devastating truth.

– How did you find him? asked Eby.

I went on explaining in cinematographic detail. I told him how we were all searching frantically in the rubble. We waited for the Civil Defense and the Israeli forces to install floodlights. It was a mess. Each of us was looking in a separate area, trying to comb the debris systematically. The Israelis were also there, and some of them were using what looked like jaws-of-life to cut through exposed, tangled rebar.

I was walking along the right side of the collapsed building with a guy from the Civil Defense moving stones, rubble, and paper. Then I noticed a light blue piece of cloth protruding from under a shattered concrete slab. I bent, grabbed it, and tried to pull it out, but it was stuck. I knelt and started digging out the dirt from around it. And I kept pulling. The more I dug, the larger the piece of cloth got. Then I started to recognize what appeared to be trousers held by a black crocodile-leather belt! I grabbed the belt and started pulling. It was a corpse. The body was in a kneeling position, with the head facing the floor. I pulled further and I noticed that his whole back had vanished and his intestines were falling out. I asked Tonto for assistance. Soon I felt a tap on my shoulders. It was Dr. Pierre Gedeon, one of Sheikh Bashir's team members. Ironically, this was the doctor who had treated me when I was shot during my fighting days.

I pulled the whole body out of the rubble. It was facing down, the face white, completely pristine and without a single hair. Two of his teeth had pierced the upper lip right below the nose and his arms were hanging back. Dr. Gedeon knelt next to me and closely examined the body.

The doctor turned his head toward one of the militiamen standing right behind him "*It's the blue saharienne*," he said. This was the outfit that Sheikh Bashir was wearing that day. Dr. Gedeon looked at me for a second. He bent over even more and looked at the left hand of the dead body. He asked me to pull the wedding ring off his finger. I reached for the hand, gently removed the ring, and handed it to him. He examined the ring thoroughly, turned it, and looked on the inside. There must have been some inscription. I've learned all of this at a later date, but while I was there I had no clue or idea that it was Sheikh Bashir.

Dr. Pierre Gedeon, still composed, spoke slowly but firmly to me. He closed his hand, squeezing the ring, nodded his head twice, and asked me to place the intestines back inside the body through the gaping hole in the back. With the help of Tonto, we place the body onto the stretcher. I tried to tuck the guts into the belly, but they were too big to fit back. He must have had a recent meal. We wrapped the corpse in a blanket, placed it into an ambulance, and I drove the remains to Hôtel-Dieu Hospital. There, we brought Sheikh Bashir's body to the Emergency entrance, where members of his family were waiting and hospital staff helped us transfer the body to a stretcher.

The funny thing was that, I still didn't realize whose body it was. I guess the stress and the adrenaline rush had blurred my thinking. Despite all the discussions and telltale signs, I still was not aware that I found the remains of Sheikh Bashir Gemayel.

We had nothing left to do there, so we returned to 102. At the entrance of 102, there were Dino and Boxer. Dino rushes toward me shouting:

– *You jerk! Why did you take him to Hôtel-Dieu?*

– *What the fuck are you talking about?* I said.

– *Bashir Gemayel! The President is dead!* Dino replied. *And you took him to Hôtel-Dieu instead of the military hospital?"*

Only at that moment I knew whom it was that I just found dead.

102 was boiling. Everybody was running around, shouting. Radios buzzed and phones were ringing.

I had tears in my eyes. Eby was incredulous and Mom was totally numb. They were clearly seeing the proverbial "light at the end of the tunnel" slowly fade to black. I felt close to Sheikh Bashir because back in his fighting days, he was in charge of my military camp. He was a great inspiration and offered help and guidance to all of us young men. This was long before he even became the head of the Lebanese Forces, it was in the Don Bosco monastery training camp.

Since that day, my call sign changed unanimously at 102 from Stanley to Champ. So sad! I was no champ. I was helpless that night.

(Jad)
SABRA, CHATILA, AND REVENGE
1982

Sunday, September 19, 1982.

It was dawn and a little chilly, but a pleasant autumn day. I was in one of the first ambulances to arrive at the outskirts of the Sabra and Chatila Palestinian refugees' camps. We parked the ambulance next to a military post.

Politics never earned a place at the Red Cross. The only creed was saving lives, and that applied to 102 and to me personally. It is true that deep inside of me, I thought Palestinians are militias; but at this very moment, my humanitarian instinct and duty committed me to help and save.

Nevertheless, I remained in a dilemma. The persons I am going to rescue were exactly the same as those that, years ago, destroyed my country, our institutions, and interfered in our political life. The same militiamen whom I have to rescue and their families, are those who ruined our families and invaded our villages. They were the very men shooting at my comrades and me, and the very men I was shooting back at. I had to decide whether to withdraw from the mission or carry on with it. I must make up my mind, and fast, because the rest of my team was starting to realize how lost I was.

A few minutes passed, and then I knew what I had to do. After all, real heroes are just normal people, but the difference is that they know what to do in such crucial situations.

I decided to carry on with my mission and ignore my emotional impulse.

A number of ambulances from 101 were already there. An Operation Center was being set up on site. My team and I headed inside for our briefing. Several veterans from the Red Cross manned the Operation Center. We, first-responders, gathered around the leader and listened carefully to the briefing, conducted with the aid of a field map. We were told to prepare ourselves for shocking encounters. We would witness horrors unlike anything we had seen before in both quantity and level. To me, this sounded humorous. I had seen enough already! I had seen it all. Few knew that I used to fight.

The Operation Center leader pointed out the access and exit points for the camps. He outlined the best routes to take and the routes to avoid. He instructed the volunteers to work in pairs and never wander around alone. The task was clear: find the wounded first, if any, and prep them for evacuation to nearby hospitals. Then we would gather the dead for transfer to field morgues.

The teams would search the small houses of the shantytown-like camps; we'd search inside manholes and investigate every corner around the creepy maze forming the camps. We did not know what to expect, so we were prepared for anything. There could be traps left behind by Palestinian militias. Even Palestinian survivors might open fire at the sight of us.

My three teammates and I moved in first. As we crossed the camp's main access, it felt like we had landed on a different planet, as if our psyches were playing tricks on us while we were venturing into this dark, grim apocalypse. As we moved ahead, a powerful stench overwhelmed our senses. The smell of death was not unfamiliar, but this was different. The stench truly was unbearable. I wondered how it could have grown so strong in such a short time. It was autumn now, the weather was quite mild, almost cold, and the necessary conditions for rapid tissue decay were not favorable. We donned our gas masks and continued walking until we reached a crossroad. We stopped and looked left, right, and ahead to plan our next move.

Everything was silent and calm. The only sounds were coming from the crackling and beeping of the radio the team was carrying, and the call for prayer from a mosque somewhere toward the south. To the left, the narrow stretch looked like a dead end. We saw a couple of soldiers walking in and out from the shacks lining the filthy street and an open sewer running down the middle. Up ahead, the main street seemed to stretch on endlessly. To my right, the narrow alley was eerily calm. As I turned my head away, I noticed what looked like a leg protruding from a door. I removed my gas mask and alerted the other guys:

– *Come on. This way.*

– *What is it?* asked Hadid faintly from behind his mask, as if afraid to be heard.

I was already walking toward that door, followed by Dino. We got closer to the spot. I was right. It was a leg. The limb was hanging outside the door. It looked like a male wearing beige trousers and flip-flops. The leg was swollen, the skin dark, which meant he'd been dead for over 24 hours.

We walked until we reached the door. Before stepping in, Dino noticed a large opening on the floor to the left of the door, just by the wall. It was 5 by 3 feet wide and looked like a manhole or the access to an underground septic tank or sewer. He slowly bent over the opening and looked inside, trying to see into the pitch darkness. It was difficult with the mask on, so he removed it and slowly bent over again. This time, he jumped back and shouted in French *"Oh, mon Dieu! Oh mon Dieu!"* (Oh my God! Oh My God!)

Everyone froze for a moment, and then turned toward Dino. He had turned milky white and was panting with obvious panic in his eyes. I was the first to move closer and look inside the hole. My eyes did not need to adjust to the dark. The hole was filled with bodies, swollen, bloody, unrecognizable corpses. I pulled back abruptly. The thick smell of death was horrifying. I collapsed against the wall and vomited. I had seen grisly injuries and handled my share of corpses, but this was the first time I had vomited while on duty with the Red Cross. It took us a while to catch our breath and snap out of the shock.

– *OK, let's get to work!* says Dino.

I radioed Ops and told them we needed transport, and then asked for a ladder and a rope. *"I have a rope,"* Hadid said, pulling what resembled a grey towing cable from his duffle bag.

I picked up the radio and started pacing the street while paging Operations.

Dino took the rope and continued, *"Boxer, you take the other radio and go check that house we came to see in the first place."*

I returned and confirmed that ambulances were on their way. Dino and I put our gas masks back on and pulled surgical gloves from our pockets. We were already wearing special overalls made out of heavy-duty synthetic material, similar to what the HAZMAT teams wear. We put the gloves on and then stared at each other. The unspoken question was obvious: Who would climb down the manhole?

"Fine, I will go down!" I say reluctantly. I never understood why the worst jobs always fell up me. Everyone at 102 treated me as if I was the most cold-hearted son of a bitch at the Center. Most had some notion of my somber past during the civil war's early days, and since the Bashir Gemayel incident; I was looked upon as 102's Superman. It was true that I could handle almost any situation, but not because I was cold-hearted. I had developed such devotion for what I do, that nothing could stop me. Besides, I had lost the most important person in my life, my father, and so in a way I became nonchalant and careless.

Finding a ladder was not difficult. Most of the shack's inhabitants used wooden ladders to access their rooftops. We found one in the alley just near the house where we were standing. I sat by the manhole opening, my legs dangling into it. I looked once more at Dino and hissed but with a grin, *"You owe me one, you bastard. A big one!"*

"I know I do," Dino answers with a warm smile. He gave me a friendly tap on the shoulder while I started descending the septic tank. I was trying to find a safe foothold without having to step upon the bodies. The hole was filled with the dead – a thick pile of cadavers. It was obvious that they had been shot first and then thrown inside the tank. I started having flashbacks to my fighting days. I remembered the Somali I shot in the throat and the other between the eyes,

and the sight of dead militiamen scattered on the streets and inside bunkers. Nothing much had changed from where I stood now, only this was a different job. Moreover, it was the stench... the unbearable stench.

I slowly slipped inside the opening and vanished. I pulled out my flashlight and switched it on. I could only see within the boundaries of the narrow beam of light. My eyes needed a while to adapt to the darkness. The fetor of decay was so strong. The filtered mask could do little to block the putrid punch of death from my nostrils.

As my vision adapted to the darkness, I was able to better assess the situation. The tank was maybe 15 feet by 15 feet and roughly 10 feet deep. I stood on a small concrete ledge halfway to the base. The bodies were piled right under the manhole, further evidence that they have been thrown in. Pointing my flashlight toward the deep end of the tank, I could see dark filthy sewer water filling about a foot of the tank. At first count, I estimated the number of bodies at 10 or 12.

– Dino, hand me the towrope. I'm gonna start pulling up the first body. You'll have to help me. I can't pull it all the way up. You have to reach in and help.

– Yes, yes, OK.

I can clearly read the disinclination in Dino's voice. I lower myself further and stand on two protruding steel pipes that are dripping a black, oily liquid. I am now teetering just a few inches above the surface of the sewer water. I bend over the first body, grab it by the belt, and pull it up enough to pass the towrope around its waist and tie a knot. It was a man, and old man, in his seventies maybe, but how could I be sure? It was too dim, and the swelling and dark skin coloration didn't help. Speaking of swelling, I knew that swollen dead bodies can burst from the accumulation of gases, and I prayed that this one would stay intact.

– *OK, Dino, the first one's coming up.*

Dino bent over the opening. I pulled the body by the belt as hard as I could. Dino grabbed the rope firmly and started pulling.

I stuck the flashlight between two of the stones lining the septic tank, trying my best to point toward the bodies. Gathering all my strength, I took a deep breath, lowered my waist in a weightlifter position, grabbed the dead man by the arm, put one leg on the ladder, and pulled.

– *Keep pulling,* I shouted up to Dino.

He continued pulling the cable slowly while I climbed the ladder, holding the dead man by the wrist. I was halfway on the ladder when I hear a muffled snapping sound. I try to disregard this. What is a broken bone to a dead man? As I climbed, helped by Dino, the weight got comfortably lighter. As I reached the ledge, I looked back down to have a look at the cadaver's position, but all I saw was an arm! The snap I heard was the sound of the dead man's arm separating from the rest of the body!

– *Fuck!* I screamed. *Fuck! Dino! Are you still pulling? Wait! Let me climb out first.*

I made it out of the septic tank holding the dripping limb. I let it fall onto the floor while I tried to wipe the blood off my overall and boots. If the body on the top of the pile had reached this level of decay, the ones below, soaking in the filthy sewer, would have reached a much more advanced stage. We definitely needed help. Professional help and equipment!

The rest of the team was in the house where I had seen the leg. Inside, an entire family of seven lay dead. The leg we saw probably belonged to the father. It looked like he was trying to push the assailants away when he got killed, because we found the rest of the family at the far end of the shack, in a combined living room and kitchen area. There was the mother and five children, three girls and two boys. Two of the children, a boy and a girl were babies, maybe between 4 and 5 years old. The mother was still holding the girl. Few women were massacred in the camps, but exceptions did occur.

When Dino came calling the team, he finds them running in circles like novices, still trying to overcome the shock and organize themselves.

It was now 7:30 a.m. and we had been in the camp for less than an hour. This would be a very long day.

Two ambulances finally arrived. They have stripped most of their cabins' interior to accommodate the bodies of the dead. Dino and I showed them the location of the septic tank. With the help of four more first-responders, we pulled out the corpses and laid them on the floor. We frisked each one for any identification and attached serial number toe-tags. The final count from the septic tank amounted to 72 bodies.

While prepping the bodies for transfer to morgues, an old woman approached me. She was yelling, waving her hands, and pulling her hair. "*My husband! My husband is here!*" Barefoot, she was now pacing swiftly toward me, and I faced her with my arms forward, a signal for her to keep her distance.

– Easy lady, easy! Where's your husband? How do you know he is here?

– They killed him and threw him here. I saw them. I must find him!

As she got within an arm's length from me, I became repulsed by her foul smell and instinctively stepped back. Her long traditional light blue dress with floral designs was spattered with dark and filthy spots. Her face was smudged, and her hair was in a mess under the once-white scarf hanging around her neck.

– Ma'am, where were you? Were you hiding?

– Yes, yes. I was hiding under the truck.

– The truck? Which truck?

– Back there in front of my home. They took him and I followed them from afar. They brought all the men here, shot them one by one, and threw them into this tank.

She turned her head, pointed to the septic tank, and froze with horror in her eyes.

– Bilal? Oh my God! Bilal! That's him, that's him. That's my husband!

She ran toward the bodies splayed across the floor and fell over one of them before any of us could stop her. I tried pulling her off the corpse, but she clung to it and fought me.

– Lady! Lady, listen to me. Listen to me, how do you know it's him? How do you know it's your husband? These bodies are not recognizable.

– I know my Bilal. That's him. Check ... check and you'll see.

– *How can we do that?* I said, still struggling to pull her off the body.

The corpse was swollen tight and could burst at any time.

– *He had a surgery few years ago, an appendicitis. Check for the scar on his belly. It's there. Check, check,* begged the woman.

I stared at Dino with a questioning look. He answered me by lifting his shoulders up.

– *Ok, ma'am, we will take a look,* I said, *but promise me to stay over there until we're done.*

The woman reluctantly stood against the facing wall. One of the volunteers stayed with her. Dino and I pulled a surgical scalpel from our kit and knelt on either side of the body she thought was her husband Bilal. The body was so bloated that we could not loosen the belt or buttons or even pull up the shirt. We had to see this scar to make a positive identification. We would use the scalpel to cut through the clothes and uncover the dead man's lower abdomen.

– *Let's do this and get over with it,* I said. Over my shoulder, I could see the woman staring back at us. *Dino, I'll kill you if you go away this time!*

Dino held the edge of the filthy T-shirt covering the torso, and I started cutting through the fabric from the bottom up. The cotton shirt was so stretched that it sheared open wide on either side, revealing the man's belly, swollen with fluids and gas, so swollen that his bellybutton was exaggeratedly protruding. The absurdity almost made me chuckle, which felt odd among all this gore.

Dino held the trousers at the waist while I inserted the

scalpel under the belt, right above the zipper and left of the belt buckle. This was an unforgiving mistake. By inserting the scalpel from the bottom up toward the abdomen, and oblivious of the fact that I was bringing a razor-sharp blade in contact with a swollen belly ready to burst, I was in for an unpleasant surprise.

I pushed the scalpel under the belt and nudged it forward. The tip of the blade hit the tight, darkened belly skin that has been hardened and thinned 24 hours after death. The scalpel slid all the way under the belt and punctured the skin. The man's abdomen burst in a muffled sound, sending body tissue and fluid all over Dino and me. The monstrosity of the stench overwhelmed the filter of our gas masks. Repulsed, I let go of the scalpel and fell backward onto my buttocks. Dino crawled backward on his hands and feet, turned, fell onto his knees, yanked off his mask, and started vomiting.

The woman who claimed to be the dead man wife struggled with the first-responders, but they managed to hold her back. Once we caught our breath, we somehow returned to our task. The abdomen was flat now, with a hole where the bellybutton had been. The putrid gas had escaped through this channel from his bellybutton down to his groin. Now we could try to view whether the man had a surgery scar without cutting the belt. He did have a scar, an uncommonly long one for appendicitis. This is Bilal. They tell the lady, who still insists on checking for herself before leaving cursing loudly, crying, and still pulling her hair.

Shortly before 3:00 p.m., the team headed back to the entrance of the camps to switch shifts. We reached Operations and entered the decontamination and cleaning tent. Everyone had to enter the tent and get sprayed profusely with a special disinfectant mixed with water and dispensed through a pressure hose before we could remove our overalls. Dino went in and then exited less than a minute later. He removed his overalls and threw them into a hazardous material collection bin at the entrance of the tent. As for me, I was not allowed in the tent! I was so dirty, so contaminated with organic matter, that they sprayed me outside the tent, in the middle of the street. Everyone stood there making fun of me; I did a better job laughing at myself.

The american embassy building after the tragic massive explosion.

(Jad)
M.A.S.H.
1983

Monday, April 18, 1983 - 1:03 p.m.

The area around the American Embassy in West Beirut was slowly becoming the stronghold of Palestinians and other strongly anti-American factions. The embassy, of course, was an ideal target for terrorists.

It was a sunny day and the beautiful West Beirut seaside causeway was bustling with commuters, couples taking a walk, Sudanese pistachio sellers, and "kaak" merchants with their three-wheeled carts. Here and there you could see an old man fishing, or another just watching the horizon smoking a "Bafra" filterless cigarette – innocent people, many with no specific purpose, enjoying a sunny spring day.

At the American Embassy the security apparatus was still too rudimentary to scan thoroughly every soul entering or exiting the building. The latter was a six-story horseshoe-shaped structure, located between few other buildings and overlooking the Mediterranean. Although not visually appealing, it was quite impressive because it stood tall among shorter and older buildings.

At 102, it was a slow day. Team 5 was on shift and taking it easy. At 1:05 p.m., the radio barks:

– *102, 102...101.*

– *101, 102.*

– *102, scramble to American Embassy immediately. Big explosion. Many casualties. Send all backups.*

– *101, acknowledged. Moving now.*

The slow-moving day turned into mayhem at 102. The American Embassy was located within a 20-minute ride from 102.

I was in Team 5. It is always a paradoxical situation at the Red Cross. The thrill of going on a mission is equal, if not more thrilling, to the dramatic situation itself. The entire Team 5 and I were thrilled. A mission to the American Embassy! This was a first time for all of us. We always heard how hard it was to get to the embassy, how strict and secure it was. The Ambassador was the most powerful figure in Lebanon, definitely more than any other politician back then. So, the idea alone was a mission for us. Also, it has always been my dream to go to the USA. For us Lebanese, USA was the most powerful country in the world, producing the most important businesses and businessmen. We all had the "American Dream", but we all knew that it was a dream indeed.

102 also called for backup from other teams. Anyone available on that normal workday joined us. When the ambulances from 102 reached the embassy, first-responders from 101 were already on site. It was the kind of destruction seldom seen in Lebanon. There had been terrorist attacks before, but not on that scale. The whole building facade had collapsed. It was raining paper. Curtains flew like flags inside the gaping holes of the structure. Rubble blocked the street and smoke from the fires and debris filled the dusty air. It was an apocalyptic sight. Bystanders watched with awe and fear, speechless, while others rushed in a chaotic mess to try rescuing the wounded.

We learned that it was a suicide attack. A van filled with explosives somehow gained access to the embassy's main entrance and managed to park under the portico where it exploded. Death was everywhere. Bodies on the ground and lower floors had been catapulted across the street. Bloody limbs were scattered on the floor, atop parked cars, on walls, and in the branches of trees lining the corniche. This was the sight of pure fear looking you in the eye.

At first, we met with the teams from 101 to be briefed and help organize a triage center. We then split in teams to initiate the search and rescue. By the time we entered the building, the Civil Defense was already there. It was a messy scene as we tried our best to remove the dead and wounded.

Meanwhile, rumors were already circulating about the American Ambassador and other high-ranking officials still trapped inside. Everyone, including me, was looking for them. Few knew that he and his top-surviving aides had been briskly airlifted in helicopters to Amman, Jordan. Three Lebanese Red Cross volunteers were on that chopper.

The total death toll from the embassy attack tallied at 63, of whom 32 were Lebanese embassy staff and 14 were innocent passersby. Seventeen Americans died; and 120 people in total were injured.

I cannot help asking myself the reason for all that. Why, when you're out of the military circle and in the humanitarian side, death (whoever it inflicts) makes you suffer. Despite the so-called adrenaline rushes after every mission, it always ended with painful hell.

Smoke could be seen from miles away, rising above the marines barrack hours after the tragedy.

(Eby)
M.A.S.H. 2
1983

Sunday, October 23, 1983.

Beirut is fast asleep. On that rainy last day of the week, the Lebanese Dream of waking up to a new hope is shattered, once more. Since 1975, we have been chasing our yearning for peace, seeking it in the dimmest piece of news, word of mouth, or even the sermon of a priest at Sunday mass. Most have got addicted to predictions and horoscopes, anything that can provide the slimmest chance of seeing the civil war end. So far, only deceptions.

In a society mostly built on faith, some are starting to doubt, even lose their faith. Countless are the nights when I lie in bed, staring at the ceiling, praying to God. All I ask of Him is to either end the madness or help us strengthen our weakening faith in Him. Jad and I were raised in a practicing Christian Catholic family. Every Sunday we went to church, first with Dad and Mom, and later with Mom. Then, we stopped, or at least I did. My faith has indeed been shaken. Although I kept praying every night, I took the decision to speak to God directly. No intermediary, no churches, no priests; just Him and me. And now, I can tell Him things. I can tell Him what I am scared of; I can be honest with Him. Strangely enough, I could feel Him listening to me more than when I went to church.

This Sunday is different in the way my wishes, prayers, and hopes were shattered. At 6:20 a.m. on that cloudy Sunday morning, 241 American Marines and 58 French soldiers were killed, and with their demise comes the demise of hope.

Two trucks loaded with explosives ran into the American and French Peacekeeping Forces headquarters and detonated. The blasts generated a tremor felt by the Beirut residents, who thought it was an earthquake at first.

Within the Beirut Airport vicinity, the 1st Battalion 8th Marines under the 2nd Marine Division had established headquarters in a vacated four-story building. A narrow winding road that leads to the premises is guarded by a checkpoint. The sentries are expecting a water delivery truck that day, but instead, the yellow Mercedes truck loaded with gas-enhanced explosives equivalent to 6 tons of TNT speeds past the guards, straight into the building's entrance and explodes.

The blast lifts the entire massive structure up in the air, detaching it from its foundation columns, each measuring 15 feet in diameter. The structure falls back on itself, flattening the floors upon each other like a deck of cards, and killing 241 soldiers.

Most of Beirut residents are still sleeping, dreaming of better days. The last couple of years were not very rewarding, and between invasions and internal feuds, the coming years are not very promising either. When they do wake up, it is to the news of the blasts. By then, all rescue services are scrambled to both locations. Civil Defense, Firefighters, and the Red Cross are mobilized and put on extreme high alert.

At 6:45 a.m. the home phone rings. A shock! The already archaic telephone network in Lebanon is rapidly decaying due to the raging war and lack of maintenance. Besides, who could be calling at this hour? Both Jad and I jump out of bed and rush to the only telephone set in the main entrance lobby. I make it there first and pick up the handset. It is the Red Cross Operations Center. They are calling all the off-duty volunteers and asking whoever could to immediately rally at 101 and 102. I ask why, but operator refuses to tell me over the phone:

– *Don't you listen to the news man?* he barks on the phone.

– *Uumm, I do, but you just woke me up, remember?*

– *Yeah, whatever, just get your asses over here. Pronto.*

– *Fine. Be there in 5 minutes.*

I hang up and tell Jad, who was poking me all the time inquiring about what was going on.

We put on our overalls and get ready to leave. We have been provided with brand new orange overalls recently to replace the white bibs. They carry a large red cross in a white circle on the back, and reflective stripes on the sleeves and legs. They make us look like pros and we are very proud to wear them. At the same time, we were each given the Red Cross round badge and an official ID card bearing a mug shot, serial number, and blood type. From there on, I am Number 1428/102.

Mom, who is already awake, is having her morning coffee and listening to the news on Voice of Lebanon. I rush to the small transistor radio and raise the volume.

– Jad! Come listen to this!

This is how we found out about the incident that morning. Mom refuses to let us leave without breakfast. So, we both reluctantly made ourselves two processed cheese sandwiches and promised to eat them on our way to 102. As usual, Mom is worried seeing us both leave. It is never easy for her, but she rarely brings up the subject.

102 feels like a beehive. People running around, bumping into each other, shouting orders, and carrying material. Preparation for the shifts schedule seems well underway. We are questioned about our availability starting the next morning, Monday, based on which the 12-hour rotation shifts will be established.

– Why all the hassle? How big is that thing? I ask Boss who is already there since 6:00 a.m. it seems.

– Eby, it's huge. From what we know, the whole building came down and we're estimating 300 to 500 casualties. That's what we have been told by Operations after consulting

with the Americans and the French. So, this is not a one off. It might take days.

I stand there for a while, lost and puzzled. Around me, first-responders are running between the radio room and the supplies depot. It is noisy and messy, and I don't see Jad anymore. I am standing in the middle of the central hall, a huge room that serves as two living rooms in the old Lebanese-style house. Sounds turn into echoes, and everything is surreal. I am scared, not from the missions, but from what lies ahead for my generation and me. I am 23 years old. All I wanted is to live, have fun, and dream of things every man in his 20s longs for. Instead, my dreams are about the end of war, being able to have a good meal, or call my girlfriend over the phone and spend hours talking. My dreams are about returning home every evening from work alive, or about having a shelling-free good night sleep. This is not what I am supposed to dream about. This is not ambition.

After consulting with my team, I decide to go to work the next morning and join the night shifts instead. Having a job in Lebanon is a luxury, let alone a steady one. I have been with an Advertising agency, for almost three years now. The last thing Lebanese think of during the civil war is Advertising. They had nothing left to advertise. The management had to fire people repeatedly to cut on costs. By June 1983, they offered the remaining staff two options; stay and get half a salary for an indefinite period or resign and get their end of service benefits. Everyone decided to leave, except me. The agency is running now with only my boss, Nizar, and me on board. I am doing the job of client servicing, graphic design – which is my actual job, secretary and even janitor. But hey! I had a job in Lebanon, and I cannot afford to stay without one. I am helping the family with the finances, and most importantly, I have committed to Aline, my wife-to-be to be wed on the January 5, 1985, 14 months from now. Much is at stake, too much to allow my love for 102 to win over.

At 10:00 a.m., I am informed by Operations that I have been assigned to night shifts at what is now called M.A.S.H 2. The Red Cross decides to adopt the M.A.S.H code name for incidents pertaining to the Americans on Lebanese soil. My first shift is set for Tuesday, October 25, starting at 6:00 p.m. until 6:00 a.m. the day after. The French have declined our help and decided to take care of their own casualties.

Monday is always a very stressful day. Not being able to take part in the action is torturing me. I spend the day at work trying to call 102 and inquiring about the rescue progress. I could not get any work done. The disasters are all over the news. At 5:00 p.m. sharp, I leave work and head straight to 102 to spend the evening there and be briefed in preparation for my shift the next day.

Tuesday comes. I wake up, prepare my gear and leave for work. I will not return home, instead, I will head straight to 102 and from there to M.A.S.H 2. My shift is scheduled to depart at 5:00 p.m. sharp. Despite the tragic nature of the event, my excitement and anticipation are at a peak. We are young and full of energy, and with an insatiable craving for "action".

My day at work is even less productive than yesterday's. I leave at 3:00 p.m. after informing my boss who mumbles, objects a little, but could not refuse. I reach 102 at 3:25 p.m. The night shift team members are starting to arrive; Boss, Mama, me, Eiffel, and finally Skinny.

Once everyone is present, Boss asks us to gather in the dining room to brief us. By then, Boss is Team 1 leader. He is perfectly fit for the job and everyone loves and respects him. Boy, did he have quirks. Who doesn't? Boss is a very introverted person. Authoritative yet with a heart of gold, he knows how to run the team, deals with everyone's character, and still manages to bring some order to a bunch of Smurfs. I have known Boss since our Scouts days. We were, and still are, neighborhood friends. We also went to the same schools during our final years.

– Guys. We have to be very careful. This is no ordinary mission.

– What's so special about it, I say, *aside from the fact that they are Americans?*

– First of all, there's the trip. We have to cross the Khaldeh Triangle, and you know how "hot" it gets there. Then, we used to have our turret light on to signal our presence and avoid sniper fire, but snipers started having fun aiming at the blue light. So now, we have to drive blind. No lights at all whatsoever.

– And how are we supposed to see where we're going? asks Mama.

– I have no clue. The roads are traitorous, there's rubble everywhere and we have to be careful. I'll drive. You all take the Kevlar helmets and gas masks. It seems the stench is unbearable there.

It has been raining for the past 2 days, which accelerates the decay of corpses still under the rubble. Rumors are circulating about people vomiting and almost fainting because of the spreading foul odors. Boss continues:

– You have to know something all of you. The Marines like us a lot. As of now, the Red Cross is the only rescue service allowed on the site. The Civil Defense has been denied access.

– Fuck man! This is sick! Says Eiffel.

– Yeah. So anyway, we have to behave perfectly well, remain polite, and most importantly follow the orders of the people in charge there. This is a crime scene and you've all watched TV and saw how Americans handle crime scenes. If you find anything, any object or artifact, report it immediately. If you find a body, do not, I repeat DO NOT handle it alone. Call for help. Always wear your gas masks while working and stay alert. It's gonna be a long night.

– Tell me about it, I mumble, *I have to be at work tomorrow at 8:30 a.m.*

– Good, says Mama with a large smile, *at least you know what to do if your boss injures you!*

We leave the dining room to get ready. It is 4:15 p.m. We are departing in exactly 15 minutes. We will take the 178, so Boss and I go run the checklist on the ambulance and make sure everything we need is there.

At 4:30 p.m., everyone is in the ambulance. Boss is driving with Eiffel next to him. Mama, Skinny, and I sit in the back. Boss is not sure we would make it; the snipers have been very active lately.

The itinerary took us through one of the hottest and most dangerous zones of the capital. First, we have to go through Jnah in West Beirut, a stronghold for Sunnis militias and Syrian army. The crossing from East to West Beirut happens through the Green Line, a virtual border splitting the capital in two halves since the start of hostilities in 1976. Very few official routes are open for crossing and even then, shutting these passages can happen at any time and without warning. We first cross the Christian militias' checkpoint at the edge of the Beirut Central District, commonly known as downtown, enter West Beirut and drive to Hamra Street in West Beirut and down to the seaside of Jnah. We cross a Muslim militia's checkpoint, and then drive toward the no man's land of the infamous Khaldeh Triangle.

West Beirut never made me feel comfortable. The Red Cross is not clearly perceived by everyone as an unbiased humanitarian organization, and some fanatics still translate the cross in the logo as defiance. They think of the Red Cross as a purely Christian organization. Of course, none of that is true. The logo of the Red Cross is a simple reversal of the Swiss flag; Switzerland being the native nation of Henry Dunand, the founder of the humanitarian organization. Go tell that to those throwing stones at you!

It is Sunset prayer time for Muslims and the streets are virtually empty, except for a few armed militiamen holding vigil. After Jnah, we reach Khaldeh Triangle, the intersection between the roads leading from Beirut toward the South or the Chouf mountains. The Triangle is a strategic point and the belligerents are fiercely fighting to win and hold that position. So far, none of the warring factions have succeeded, which makes the location one of the hottest in the civil war and we have to go straight through it. It is now 4:50 p.m., and almost dark already because of the winter light. Boss slows down and parks the ambulance under the defunct bridge that crosses the Triangle. There, safely hiding next to one of the bridge's massive pillars riddled with bullet holes and political graffiti, we assess the situation. He turns off all the ambulance lights and dims the instrument panel to the lowest.

– *Helmets on everyone,* he orders.

– *This is gonna be messy,* whispers Eiffel sipping on his cigarette.

– *Finish your cigarette and extinguish it immediately,* barks Boss.

– *Bon, Bon, ça va!* (Alright, alright) replies Eiffel with his typical snobbish French accent.

Cigarette light is the cause of many casualties during war. The light from a cigarette tip can be seen from as far as a mile. It constitutes a perfect aim for snipers. Eiffel takes a long last puff and throws the butt. We scan the area one last time looking for tracer bullets and explosions echo. So far so good.

– *This is it,* says Boss, *let's go.*

We slowly leave the safe haven of the bridge pillar and venture through the open area of the Khaldeh Triangle. Boss cannot drive any faster; the road is littered with large debris. There are concrete boulders that fell from the bridge, explosion craters that could swallow an entire car, shipping containers used to block the road or create bunkers (some with large RPG, Rocket Propelled Grenade, blast holes in them), and the wrecks of charred cars. Boss maneuvers among the obstacles in almost total darkness. Eiffel tries to help as much as he could, while the rest of the team looks through the side windows of the ambulance. These are 8 very tense minutes that every ambulance going to M.A.S.H 2 has to go through.

I keep silent most of the trip. Even Boss notices and

asks how come I am not cracking any of my usual jokes. I am thinking about how it would be like at M.A.S.H. 2. I was never involved in a mission of this scale, let alone one with the US Armed Forces. I am trying to anticipate the reaction of the Marines toward us. We are Lebanese after all, and we are the immediate cause of their presence here, as well as their losses.

We finally cross the Triangle. Boss switches the ambulance's lights back on and we cruise toward the airport. It is already 4:58 p.m.

We reach Beirut International Airport's main street that leads to the terminals, and from there make a left toward the Marines compound's heavily guarded main gate. Sentries are on full alert, and one can notice how edgy they are as we approach the checkpoint. I later found out that prior to the attack, they were kept under what is labelled as "Rules of Engagement" with weapons on "Condition 4", meaning they had no magazines in their firearms and no round in the chamber, which rendered an immediate reaction virtually impossible. That's how the infamous explosives-laden truck managed to cross the first line of defense.

At the checkpoint, one of the sentries raises his arm in a sign for us to stop. Boss complies. The Marine approaches the ambulance from the driver's side and politely asks us to stop the engine and step out of the ambulance. We immediately execute. The ambulance is thoroughly checked, so are our badges. We are then carefully frisked while one of the sentries calls his Command Center to get us clearance. Once this is done, the 178 drives into the compound. The dirt road leading to the site is lit with floodlight units mounted on their own power generators, casting dramatic shadows. As Boss negotiates the last turn, the horror unfolds between two rubble mounds, like an apocalyptic vision.

A dozen floodlight units, each with eight daylight bulbs are evenly scattered around the site, forming a large circle. The power of the lights is of such intensity that the area surrounding the site is pitch black. From afar, the site looks like a scene straight out from Spielberg's *Close Encounters of the Third Kind*. I am a big fan of science fiction and this is my all-time favorite movie.

At the center of the floodlights, a crater 65 feet across and 33 feet deep signals the exact spot where the suicide bomber detonated the truck. Right in front of the crater, the once four-story structure is reduced to the height of a two-story building. The floors have collapsed on each other in an almost perfect manner. There is no way to tell where the main entrance is located. The explosion crater is the only indication.

Boss parks the ambulance to the left of the site in a specially designated area. Mama opens the side door to step out, and almost immediately the stench invades the ambulance. A mixture of wet soil and rotten eggs, the smell of death. I step out and freeze in awe. For a minute, I am mesmerized and unable to move. A chill runs down my spine. The only time I have seen anything similar was in movies. Despite the morbid circumstances, the site has some majesty to it. It is beyond description. Boss finally breaks the silence:

– *Let's get to work.*

I slowly start to walk toward the lights, scanning the area around me and trying to get acquainted with the situation.

Behind the collapsed building, the Marines have setup the triage and morgue site, a large area lined with tables with black body bags on top of each. There, the remains of killed soldiers are stripped and cleaned, their dog tags removed and referenced, and their personal belongings gathered in special bags to be returned to their families. To the left, close to where the ambulance is parked, a makeshift table made with cinder blocks and a door panel carries coffee and teakettles. Next to the table, fresh water dispensers are on the floor.

Marines are busy cleaning up around the site, searching for clues and gathering official papers and other objects that were dispersed by the blast. Personal belongings are also found scattered. Photos of loved ones, pens, books, clothing, and toothbrushes littered the site.

We reach the building. Standing in front of the collapsed structure, one could grasp the magnitude of the tragedy. This used to be a massive building. The floors measure around 150 feet by 70 feet each, and all four of them have collapsed on top of each other like pancakes. I am now staring at a sandwich of four slabs neatly layered. Ladders were placed at specific intervals to allow rescue teams to climb on top. Bulldozers and cranes are rumbling, working very meticulously at removing pieces of concrete. They have to be careful not to jeopardize the lives of the rescuers, or hit a survivor, or one of the dead still under the rubble. Once a slice of the roof slab is removed, the excavators move to another part of the site while we start searching the freshly uncovered debris helped by Marines. This is what my colleagues and I will be doing for the next 12 hours.

Boss, Mama, and I climb one of the ladders while Eiffel and Skinny take the one next to us. The rescue work is still being done at the topmost floor. The excavators have just finished removing a large chunk of concrete from the corner of the building to our left, facing the triage center. We head there and start helping the Marines looking for bodies. There is no technique per se; we have to rely on visual clues most of the time or follow the smell. Although the floodlights illuminated brightly the scene, it is still artificial white light and the multitude of shadows cast by every spotlight unit does not quite help to discern shapes and mostly colors. While looking at the debris facing one of the floodlights, we are blinded by the beam and have to place our hands on our foreheads to block it.

At first sight, it looked like a communication room. There are crushed radio receivers' chargers, some with the sets still hooked in. We also can notice flattened desks and large communication apparatus. Higher-ranking officers are overlooking the rescue efforts just in case classified material is found. These would have to be immediately handed over to them.

I get down on my knees and start removing blocks of shattered concrete and throwing them in an open and already cleared area to my left. Muddy and rainwater-soaked fatigues, papers and even sandwiches litter the site. I then notice that the stench is growing stronger, to a point where it becomes hard for me to breathe. Boss, who is next to me helping, instructs me to put on my gas mask. He had his on already and I comply without hesitation.

It is very cold and humid, and it kept drizzling intermittently, soaking everyone. The special Red Cross orange plastic coat helps keep me dry, but reduces mobility and maneuverability. Every effort becomes a daunting task. To make things worse, breathing with the gas mask on is strenuous, not that it helped much. A veteran Red Cross friend gave me a good tip: *"Spray surgical spirit or cologne on the mask filter,"* he told me, *"it helps reduce the smell dramatically"*. Great, now where could I get some cologne on top of a four-story collapsed building...?

The stench is unbearable now and the gas mask is not able to hold it back anymore. I knew that I was very close to unearthing another body. Boss calls the rest of the team and we all get on our knees and start scraping the debris with our bare hands. One Marine is also there removing smaller pieces of concrete. He notices a piece of paper emerging from under the rain-soaked mud like rubble. Thinking it might contain classified data, he reaches and starts gently pulling it out of the rubble, but it would not come out. He pulls harder, but in vain. He starts digging around it to release it and freezes. What resembles a finger is protruding from the rubble. He starts digging further, and reveals a hand holding the paper. He stops:

– *Guys, guys! Over here!*

Everyone stops and joins the Marine in digging around the hand. Mama could not take it anymore. She snaps off her mask, runs to the opposite corner and starts vomiting. I am not feeling any better, but somehow manage to hold back.

This is the first time I ever smell death. It is indescribable. Jad once told me that anyone exposed to the stench of death would live with it for the end of his or her days. Even today, over 30 years later, every time I think of death, the smell comes back making me nauseous.

As we dig further, the body of a soldier starts to emerge slowly. He is lying face down, his right arm completely stretched to the front, while his left is bent toward his face holding the piece of paper. His right leg is also bent at a right angle. He is in his army fatigues with not many insignias on them, which indicates he probably is a private.

One of the high-rank officers bends over the body still being excavated and pries the piece of paper out of the hand clutching it. He stands up, unfolds the paper, holds it up to his face and turns in the direction of one of the floodlights to see clearly what is written on it.

A few seconds later, he stops, drops the hand holding the paper, and looks at the body for a while:

– *He was writing a letter to his loved one. He did not finish it.*

We all stop for a minute and look at the body, and then resume work.

The head of the victim is completely flattened and the skin on the skull is reduced to folds. As if you stripped the body of its bones, it is totally intact but perfectly flat.

We finish unearthing the corpse and stand up to pull it out and place it on a stretcher. Eiffel and Skinny have already brought one and placed it behind the working team. One Marine stands in front of the head and places his hands under the body's shoulders, while Boss and another Marine hold the body at the waist on either side. I place my hands slightly below the victim's knees to try to grab both legs.

Boss gives the order to lift on three. We pull in unison and the body comes off like a slab. It is completely stiff, as stiff as plank of wood. We are holding the body 3 feet off the ground and yet the corpse keeps its exact same position, his right arm and left leg stretched, and his left arm and right leg bent. It is a very strange sight and feeling; carrying a flattened, cold, and stiff body of what was, a day ago, a young healthy Marine.

We gently place the corpse on the stretcher with his arms and legs protruding and carry it to the edge of the collapsed roof. Two of the Marines climb down the ladder while Eiffel climbs a few stairs down. The rest of us stay up as we start slowly lowering the stretcher, taking care not to slide the cadaver off it. It takes us a good 15 minutes to achieve the maneuver and deliver the stretcher to the Triage Center. There, one of the Marines' medical staff removes the victim's dog tags, notes the matriculation numbers and time on a large log book, and asks the soldiers to prep the body for wrapping. It is now 7:55 p.m. This is going to be a long night.

As the excavators take over once again, we manage to get a short break. Everyone realizes that we have not yet reached the dorms yet. This is where most of the casualties are expected to be. The blast occurred in the early morning when everyone was still asleep. The terrorists were vicious enough to realize that. According to the Marines, the dorms are located on the second floor of the collapsed building. The excavators are still working on the third floor, where the communications and briefing halls are. The rest of team climbs down the ladder and heads toward the coffee stand. I am still standing on the roof slab of the collapsed floor watching the machines in action. Then, a sudden flash catapults me back to 1978...

I don't remember the exact date anymore; I guess it was around September. The civil war is at its second year. I am 17 years old and work night shifts as an editor at a teens' magazine, "Flash".

I do not own a car yet. The walk back home is downhill and relaxing. As I walk, the sights, sounds, and smells of the neighborhoods each have a story. I try to guess these stories. Here, a housewife is preparing dinner; I can tell from the smell of garlic filling the air. There, behind "Tergal" curtains, white lights flicker and cast shadows against the walls and onto the balcony. Some guy in his pajamas must be sitting on a brown felt couch, watching the news on his old TV set.

That day in September, I finish preparing the magazine's next issue's content and get ready to head home. I clean up the dining table-cum-desk, switch the lights off, and leave. My walk home is preset. After 2 years, I managed to trace an optimized route that takes 20 minutes on average.

It is dark outside; the streetlights are not working anymore. Since the start of the civil war, it was safer to keep the lights off, as they were ideal sniper targets. The streets are silent and empty. I can hear the sound of TV sets in the background reciting the day's events on primetime news.

As I reach the short stretch that leads to Charles Malek Avenue, I remember that I am out of shampoo. We don't often get the chance to show some appreciation for all that our Mother is doing for us, so I thought it would be nice to get it myself. There is a pharmacy just a few feet back and luckily, it is still open. I walk the short distance back and step in just as the lady at the counter is getting ready to close shop. She's nice enough to re-open the cash counter for me, while telling me how lucky I am. I buy my Head & Shoulders, thank her, and leave. I resume my walk toward Charles Malek. I swiftly cross the desolate wide intersection and start walking down the Accaoui's long slope. I reach the Sursock alley exit when a deafening explosion makes me instinctively drop down and crouch against the Sursock palace fence with my hands over my head. I could not hear anything anymore, just a piercing high-pitch whistle inside my ears. My heart is beating so fast I can feel my pulse in my eyes and temples. I am so scared and confused. I remain hiding against the wall looking for a passerby, a car, anything that tells me I am not the only survivor left on the planet. Nothing, not a soul is around, just the high-pitch whistle followed by utter silence.

I can't recall how long I remained hiding against that wall. I am certain that Mom and Jad also heard the blast. They know that I am on my way home by now and they must be panicking. I stand up and start walking slowly looking left and right as if being chased. As I reach a soft bend in the street, I could peer into the remainder of the Accaoui slope leading down to Gemmayzeh. In the darkness, I notice shimmering glows toward the end of the street casting light on a rising thick dark smoke. I am puzzled at first. If it was a mortar shell, its blast could not be powerful enough to suck the air out of my lungs from that far away. Besides, that did not sound or feel like any mortar.

I keep carefully walking down, instinctively brushing against the buildings' walls. As I reach the "Le Vieux Quartier" restaurant building to my right, the most expensive restaurant in Beirut, the immense tragedy unfolds.

Toward the end of Accaoui, the road widens before narrowing down again as it intersects with Gemmayzeh Street. To the left, there is the Christian Forces' SKS barracks, and facing it on the opposite side, a street leads to the St. George Hospital. In the middle of the wide stretch, burning cars litter the asphalt, fires and rubble everywhere. Thick black smoke, the stench of burning rubber and fuel suffocate me. I cover my mouth and nostrils with my sleeve. In the middle of road, a car, the make of which is not discernible anymore, is at an angle as if making a turn toward the St. George Hospital. Inside, the charred body of the driver is leaning on the metal rim of the still burning steering wheel, with his or her left arm hanging outside the window. In the passenger seat, a child, also burning and unrecognizable, still is in a seated position and with the head leaning toward the door. Other cars are filled with their dead occupants. The right back door of another vehicle, facing me, is open and a man is lying, half of his body out of the car. He might have still been alive and tried to climb out of the burning vehicle.

I keep walking. I do not stop; I am hardly lucid. It is the first time of my life I see mutilated dead bodies. I heard stories before, and have seen some raw footage on TV, but never in reality. The only time I ever got that close to death was when I sat next to my dead Father in bed. As I walk in the increasingly dense rubble, I keep an eye on my footsteps; fearing to trip on a piece of concrete or rebar and injure myself. As I look down in the dark, I come face to face with a severely mutilated body. I could have stepped on it. I froze. Now I am panicking. I walk around the body and unconsciously, start running down until I reach Gemmayzeh. There, I stop, turn and look back one last time at the scene.

I was 17 years old. I never purchased anything for home; Mom always did the shopping. What went through my head to step into that pharmacy and buy the shampoo?

It saved my life. Those 3 minutes, the exact same time would have taken me to reach Accaoui's bombsite, saved my life. Had I not made that stop, I would have been right at the center of the blast. The lady pharmacist was right, I am lucky.

This was the first in an endless spiral of terrorist attacks to hit Lebanon. This one was estimated at 450 pounds of explosives.

I snap out of my memories just as Mama is calling me to join the team. I wave at her and climb down the ladder heading for the coffee corner. Some soldiers are gathered around the dispensers drinking coffee or tea and chatting. No one is smiling; they all look depressed and sad. One can guess what all the discussions are about. As they see me walk closer toward the beverage corner, they politely make space for the team and me to get served. Some of the soldiers gently smile at us and nod their heads. I cannot help but engage in a discussion. I start by saying how sorry I feel for their tragedy and the rest of the team shake their heads in approval. I pour myself some hot coffee in a white foam cup and head for a slab of concrete on the floor to my right to sit for a while. Next to me, a Marine is already there with his head down, holding a cup of tea with both hands:

– Hey! Are you ok? I ask.

The soldier lifts his head suddenly startled by my presence, looks at me for a second and lowers his head back:

– Yeah. I'm ok... I mean you know.

– Yeah, I know, I reply. *It must have been hard. I'm Ibrahim by the way. You can call me Eby.*

– *Tony*, he answers with an unmistakable Latin-American accent.

– *Where were you located when it happened?*

– *I was one of the sentries, over there.* He points at the dirt road to the left that leads to the compound entrance.

– *Damn! So, you saw the truck?*

– *Yep. I did".* He pauses. *"Fuck the Rules of Engagement, man! We could've prevented it.*

– *You mean you did not shoot or anything?*

– *We could not. We were on "Condition 4".*

– *Condition 4?*

– *Yeah, no loaded weapons. No magazines in the guns.*

– *Oh! I see. And you feel guilty.*

– *Guilty?! Jesus man! We're gonna end up with 200 dead Marines.*

He nonchalantly stretches his right arm and with the palm of his hand points at the collapsed building.

– *I got friends in there, man. My whole fucking company was sleeping.*

I notice a shy tear gushing out of his right eye. He immediately wipes it off.

– *I'm so sorry, Tony.*

– *Yeah, I know. We all are. Fuck man! What have you done to this country of yours?*

For some reason, I saw this coming. This is the one-million-dollar riddle that most of the young educated populace is trying to figure out.

– *We did nothing Tony. We did nothing to our country.*

Tony lifts his head again and faces me surprised. To him, this sounded as an arrogant answer. I continue:

– *And that's exactly the problem. I've got my theory around this one, but I'll keep it to myself.*

– *No. I wanna hear it. I just wanna try and give a valid reason, a good reason to all the dead under that building.*

– *I will never be able to give you a 'good' reason. There isn't any, Tony. I can give you one answer, but it will make you even more furious about what happened.*

Tony gives me an inquisitive look, waiting for an answer.

– *You know?* I hesitantly say, *there are those who publicly and arrogantly sell their country. Then, there are those who sit on their ass and feel sorry about their country being sold. There are those who believe in the wrong cause and destroy a nation, and those who do not believe in any cause, sit on their ass and feel sorry for their destroyed nation. Here, we have both, and both are wrong. That's what is wrong with my country.*

– *And which of the two do you belong to?*

Now, that's one question I never saw coming. I always felt distant and immune from the war madness. As far as I was concerned, I never belonged here; I never felt a shred of patriotism. As far as I was concerned, I was parachuted in hostile ground. I always held a totally unjustified grudge against my parents for that.

– *Me? I belong to the second one. I sat on my ass and felt sorry all the time.*

– *But you're here now,* says Tony lowering his head again.

He pauses and then continues:

– *And that's good. That's ok,* letting a shy smile escape.

– *Yeah. I'm here now... What a paradox. I'm here to repent for sitting on my ass. Yet, I'm here to witness the consequence of just doing so.*

I stand up, still holding my cup of coffee, look at Tony, give him a tap on the shoulder and go meet the rest of the team. Tony does not bulge. He keeps sitting there staring at the floor, holding his cup of tea with both hands.

(Jad)
BURGERS AND BUMPERS
1983

Ambulances always rush to the rescue, carry the wounded and safely get them to hospitals on time. Volunteers seldom think about distance, traffic and speed.

Although greatly respected and appreciated by the community, the Red Cross is not always given all the needed assistance or support, mostly on the road. It is a trait of the Lebanese driver to monopolize the road. When driving, he or she is the uncontested king of the asphalt. There are two types of drivers in Lebanon when it comes to an encounter with an ambulance:

First, there are the leaders. They will never cede the road to anyone, not even an ambulance. They claim that ambulances use their sirens to annoy people. Therefore, instead of giving way, they keep their heading and force the ambulance to follow them, until "they" decide to let it through. During the civil war, it is highly advisable not to alienate such drivers. They usually are militiamen, bullies, or simply wannabes. In all cases, they are armed to the teeth, and carry more ammunition then brain cells. The ambulance occupants do not want to end with more than the casualty they are carrying. Unfortunately, in some cases, the ambulance does not make it on time to the hospital because of heavy traffic and similar drivers.

Then, there are the followers, less dangerous and

opportunistic. They wait for an ambulance to show up, give it way, and immediately rush behind it in its wake. The ambulance would open the road ahead, and they would make it faster to their destination. It is not uncommon to see an ambulance all lights and sirens on followed by a convoy of vehicles driving at high speed. They even honk and flash their lights nervously to make everyone else think they are part of the ambulance's convoy.

In both cases, ambulance drivers and first-responders have to cope with the pressure of the total chaos reigning on the Lebanese roads.

I was in the 178 with Joura heading down Accaoui Street, on our way back from Sassine Square where we had purchased tonight's dinner, 10 burgers with fries from The Chase restaurant. It is 7:00 p.m. on a cold but dry winter day.

We are about to reach the SKS barracks. It used to be a school ran by a charity for the underprivileged. The Lebanese Forces militia converted it into a barrack that also houses the militia's fanfare. You can hear the band rehearsing every afternoon. Facing SKS is a one-way narrow street that leads up to the St. George Hospital. One-way is not a term in the Lebanese lexicon, not during peacetime and, for sure not during wartime. Also ironically, it was the very same spot where Eby almost got killed by a huge explosion, had it not been for the shampoo he stopped to purchase.

As the Volkswagen Transporter rushes to the end of Accaoui and toward the intersection with Gemmayzeh, an old sky-blue Datsun drives out of the one-way street in the opposite direction and turns down toward Gemmayzeh. It had no taillights. The streets were never lit during the civil war, and the road was pitch black except for the headlamps of the ambulance.

The 178 reaches SKS just as the Datsun finishes its right turn, and I ram the car from behind sending it swirling and hitting the row of parked vehicles to the left. The Datsun's trunk pops open, and hundreds of steel 2-inches nails stacked in carton boxes, fly in the air and land on the ambulance and the street. The ambulance loses both its headlamps. Joura and I are spared. Wearing seat belts was mandatory in the Red Cross.

I turned on my flashers, made sure that the food is safe and stepped out of the ambulance with Joura. The Datsun's driver is fine. He escaped with few bruises to his arms and forehead. He's a carpenter, which explains the nails in the trunk. In desperation, he tells me that he just had his car re-painted and out of the body shop the day before. For Joura and me, it was pathetically hilarious, but we manage to retain our composure. We radio 102 to call an insurance surveyor to check the scene.

All that time, we were thinking of the burgers and fries that would reach the Center cold. We pulled out two burgers and two packs of fries, sat in the back of the ambulance and had dinner waiting for the surveyor.

(Eby)
FOOD FIT FOR KINGS
1983

At 102, we are not ashamed of our extravagances. We love to live, and love to show it. Team 1 is famed for turning 102 into a five-star restaurant during its Thursday night shifts.

In normal days, every team is allocated a small budget for food, enough to get a decent meal of our choice. It varies between dairy products and bread or, occasionally, we treat ourselves to a more copious meal, such as grilled chicken sandwiches from Lala, the small but famous grill house in Fassouh.

During the days of Delta, food became scarce. Supplies could not be delivered regularly and there were days where we had to eat anything we could lay our hands on. When it got really tough, even blood supplies could not reach the blood bank, let alone food.

It has been 2 days now that no one could move out of 102 except for emergency missions. Boss and I manage to make it from Delta to 102 early in the afternoon, to get supplies and visit our families in Gemmayzeh. Once we reached the center, it became impossible to leave again due to the heavy shelling, and we got stuck there.

In the evening, we manage, with the rest of the volunteers on duty, to scour the fridge for leftovers. We are lucky to have a power generator to keep the blood refrigerator running, it also helps in preserving the food in the kitchen fridge. We were hoping to make it back to Delta in the evening, but those hopes are shattered by the heavy fighting that broke as the sun came to set. We have to spend the night at 102. Boss radios Delta to inform them.

On the next morning, the battle is still raging and now we cannot even make the emergency sorties. We are all hungry, and there's nothing left to eat. Boss suddenly remembers:

– *Guys? Don't we keep biscuits and army rations in the cellar?*

– *Hey yeah!* says Boxer. *Let's check it out.*

They get the old wood ladder, lean it against the cellar access located above the living quarters. Boss climbs and vanishes between the carton boxes. A minute later, everyone hears the typical Boss laugh, which sounds more like an old Rottweiler barking.

– *Yes! Got it. Guys, someone catch the stuff. I'm gonna throw it.*

Everyone is already at the bottom of the ladder, waiting for Boss to throw the food. We look like hunger-stricken children catching food thrown from a relief truck.

Boss pops his head, throws two plastic bags, and climbs down the ladder.

We gather in the dining room, open the bags, and pull out the content. The first bag contains energy bars provided by the American Army. These are small pieces of chocolate, the size of a Mars bar, with high concentration of vitamins. It seems that one ration equals a complete meal and should provide enough energy. The second bag is full of "Tuc" salted crackers packs. Made by "LU", they're tasty and go perfectly with cheese and a good glass of wine, I think to myself.

So far so good. Until we notice the expiration date. The energy bars expired around six months ago, and the crackers are more than a year old. That was all we had, along with the small block of Hungarian "Kashkaval" cheese in the fridge, and that one was more than 3 weeks old.

We have no choice. Boss brings the cheese block and a knife. The others and I open a couple of biscuits packs. We decide to spare the energy bars for now. They might come in handy when nothing else is left. Boss tries to cut the cheese, but it's so dry and hard, the knife would not cut through. Boss never runs out of tricks. He immediately rushes to the tool room and returns with a hammer. He places the cheese on a newspaper directly on the dining table, positions the tip of the knife in its center and hits with the hammer. The block of cheese breaks into pieces like a china vase.

Everyone gets two crackers and a piece of "Kashkaval". Now, we have to find a way to chew it.

– *Are you sure we can eat this?* asks Boxer. *What if we get food poisoning?*

– *You're in the perfect place then,* I answer with a smile.

After rationing the cheese and crackers, we spare some for the evening. There won't be any lunch today. As the day passes by, the battles start slowly winding down. We decide (Boss and me) to spend a second night at 102 and leave in the morning if the situation allows it.

The next morning, the situation calms down and the

lull allows supplies to reach 102 and Boss and I to return to Delta, but not after a quick visit home.

A few months later, Delta is closed down and everyone returns to 102. At Team 1, we take the decision to organize dining nights during our shifts. We agree that on every Thursday shift, every member of the team will get his or her Mom to cook a special meal for the whole team. And so we did, creating a new tradition at 102 and the Lebanese Red Cross. Every Thursday night at 102 was a feast. "*Kibbeh bil sayniyeh*", "*Mouloukhieh*", "*Moghrabieh*", you name it, we made it, and in quantities to feed a regiment.

So renowned it became, that every Thursday, 102 would be packed with volunteers from other teams. Thursday night is party night at 102. And that's not all.

One day, Kebbeh shows up with his Mom's Filipina maid. He says that she is a great cook, and that tonight is Filipino night at 102. The maid cooks up a "Pansit" meal. A delicacy in Manila, which is prepared with pork meat, rice noodles, and spices. That was one unforgettable night at 102. We managed to keep the rumor from spreading and had a quiet and intimate Team 1 Smurfs night.

Food became another trademark of 102. Fruit cocktails that the guys would bring on their way back from missions also became a ritual. Missions to Batroun would not be complete without the city's famous lemonade.

One has to admit, creativity is a great asset in dire times, and 102 never lacked enough of it.

(Jad)
ECHO OF SOUK EL GHARB
1983

The first-responders have seen things in almost every hospital of the country. Yet, nothing prepared them to what they are about to see at Echo. "Echo" is the Red Cross call sign for the Military Hospital in Badaro, Beirut.

Battles rage in Souk El Gharb between the Lebanese Army and mercenaries from every possible nationality: Iraqis, Somalis, Syrians, Sudanese, Libyans, and others. Casualties among the soldiers are high, and battles are taking place during the winter and spring in the freezing mountains.

The Lebanese Red Cross set up an outpost in Souk El Gharb, establishing a triage center; the role of which is to prioritize casualties before the transfer to nearby hospitals or via helicopter and tanks to Echo.

I have been many times to the Triage Center, as well as to Echo. Eby has never been to Souk El Gharb.

Shifts at Echo were a 12-hour rotation. Teams from 101 and 102 would take turns, changing shifts at 6:00 a.m. and 6:00 p.m. Both Eby and I had to take the 6:00 p.m. to 6:00 a.m. shifts because of our day jobs.

At the Triage Center in "Souk el Gharb" we have established tents where casualties are brought in at an incredible pace. At night, it turns apocalyptic. Mud covered everything, and it is hard to tell thunder from bombs.

Everyone runs frantically trying to cope with the influx of the wounded and dead. But it is very hard. Most casualties are severe and the volunteers are playing God. Dispatching one before the other two hospitals can sometimes mean the certain death of the one left behind. But things have to be done methodically and the first-responders must remain calm and lucid.

Ambulances rush the wounded to relay points where they rendezvous with other ambulances to shuttle the patients to Echo. The teams sometimes go 48 hours without sleep. In some cases, armored M113 personnel carriers transport casualties straight to Echo. The M113 could penetrate deep in the front and carry large numbers of soldiers. For casualties requiring immediate transfer, army helicopters are used.

Souk El Gharb was no joy ride. All the horrors of war that one sees at the movies are replayed live... but this is not a movie. This is reality, where people really die, where people are really wounded, where soldiers cry.

I had my fill of reality.

On one evening, I was at the Triage Center. Fighting is raging on and casualties are pouring. One young soldier is brought in with his lower right side missing from the hip down. Part of his pelvis is missing and his right leg is nowhere to be found. He is bleeding profusely and the doctors are mobilized to try to save his life and what's left of him.

Kebbeh and I are busy sorting out casualties by priority before sending those who can wait to Echo, while the urgent ones are treated in the field hospital.

As the doctors were trying to save the poor soldier's remaining leg, another one is rushed in also with his right leg severely mutilated and barely hanging on to his upper thigh. The busy surgeons look at him, not knowing what to do. They cannot leave the one they're treating, nor can they ignore the newcomer. So, they decided to relieve one of the nurses in order to treat the new arrival and asked Kebbeh and me to help him.

Thrilled but somewhat worried, we both rushed to help. One of the surgeons prepping the other soldier looked at me and bluntly shouts:

– *You will have to amputate his leg. The tools and electric saw are over there. The nurse will help.*

– *Huh? What? Me?* I stutter.

– *We have no choice and we can't wait. He is bleeding profusely and can die of infection. Can you do it? Yes or no?*

– *Um, yeah, ok. I will.*

I look at the wound. The upper thigh, well above the knee, is shattered. Only a few pieces of flesh remain attached, and the thighbone is clearly visible but is still in one piece. I decide to apply first a tourniquet, thinking for a minute why it was not already done; this was part of the routine military training. All I could think of was a picture of my Dad with one leg, and what I went through when I was shot in the knee, fearing that I will eventually lose my leg. I was ready and willing to save the guy's leg whatever it takes! I grab a flexible rubber tube similar to the ones used to squeeze the artery when donating blood. I tied it around the thigh as high as I could and squeezed as hard as possible. The pulsating bleeding was slowly reduced to a halt. Then I remembered that neither Kebbeh nor I were wearing any surgical gloves or masks.

We both put on scrubs, latex gloves, and masks and get to work. The nurse had already administered a heavy anesthetic, while another checked the soldier's dog tags before rushing to get IVs and blood flasks.

I hold a sharp scalpel and start cutting the flesh stripping the thighbone. I was amazed at how I was handling it. I knew I was courageous and could handle anything, but I never thought I would be able to perform an amputation. I was traumatized and still am by that word. Actually, I never thought a doctor would ask me to do so. I was not even sure if I was doing things right, but I imagined that the only right thing now was to save the soldier's life, in any possible way. I just couldn't stop thinking of my Dad, how horrible it must have been to lose his leg during that tram accident back in 1950. For a while, I thought to myself *"Why me and not the nurse? These are experienced staff who graduated from medical schools"*. I wanted to ask this question once done, but I completely forgot.

I switched the shiny silver contraption on and heard the buzzing sound of the blade vibrating back and forth at high speed. I stared at the bone for a while hesitating. I looked at Kebbeh and the nurse; Kebbeh was gone!! He was helping someone else. The nurse nodded positively and gave me the ok to start. I held the upper thigh with my left hand and slowly brought the saw over the bone. The nurse grabbed my wrist gently and moved it a little higher over the bone to allow more flesh to cover the wound when sutured. On contact, white powder from the pulverized bone flew and a smell filled the air, similar to the one at the dentist when performing a root canal. The nurse started spraying sterilized water over the cut to lubricate. I cut slowly through the bone, until the saw went through in a snap and hit the bunk bed. I immediately switched the power off. The soldier's right leg was now completely separated from the rest of his body. I couldn't believe my eyes, couldn't believe what I just did.

"I'll take it from here," said the nurse already holding the suturing threaded curved needle. I put down the saw and pulled away. Now, I began to absorb the shock of what I just did. I took off my bloodstained surgical outfits and left the tent. In a strange way, sitting under the stars and listening to the sound of bombs and bullets was soothing.

(Eby)
THE HELICOPTER TRANSFER
1983

From Souk El Gharb and Echo to transfer missions, handling the Lebanese Army's causalities is far from average, and almost borders the surreal.

It's 5:00 a.m. on a fine spring morning. The sun is yet to rise but it's already daylight. The night before was one of the hardest. Battles raged in Souk El Gharb and the shelling of Beirut residential areas went on all night. It hasn't stopped yet.

From where I'm hiding, the mushroom clouds from explosions and fires raging in Ain El Remmaneh can be seen spiraling up in the sky, their dark grey color mixes with the orange dawn, and then slowly blends with the vivid blue of a sky anticipating the sunrise. As they gain altitude, the gliding winds bend the smoke, shaping it into apocalyptic monsters.

Mama, Nounours, Sierra, and I are at Sin El Fil's old and dilapidated train station. The concrete-covered area, as large as three football fields, constituted a perfect helicopter-landing zone. To the South, Ain El Remmaneh is burning.

Ain El Remmaneh faces Chiah in the Beirut suburbs. Both neighborhoods are an extension to the Green Line, the virtual boundary between East and West Beirut. Ain El Remmaneh is a Christian stronghold, while Chiah is a

Muslim one. Some of the fiercest battles have raged there, and still do.

Ain El Remmaneh is infamous for being where the Lebanese Civil War started. On the morning of April 13, 1975, gunmen in a speeding car fire on a church, killing four people. Hours later, the Phalangists militiamen kill 30 Palestinians commuting through Ain El Remmaneh in a bus. That day marked the start of the Civil War in Lebanon. One cannot help thinking how the bloodiest wars in history all started with a futile incident.

We are hiding on the North side of the station inside the historic Al Abed Clock. The Clock Tower used to adorn the *Nejmeh* (Star) Square in Beirut's downtown, where the House of Parliament is located. Prior to the Clock Tower, ancient Roman ruins were found there and kept for a while as a monument to Beirut's history. Later, the ruins were moved away and the famous Clock Tower was erected. Considered a precious monument, it was dismantled stone by stone and re-erected in the Sin El Fil old train station until it could be brought back home.

At the base of the yellow stone tower, a small 3 feet by 3 feet rusty metallic door gives access to the maintenance staircase. We're cramped inside, sticking our heads out every once in a while to check on the situation.

We've been waiting there for over half an hour now. Losing patience, I step outside to smoke a cigarette, waiting for the squeaking radio to give us an update. It is chilly and humid. I can hear the mortar shells whistle above my head, and land not far away, in Ain El Remmaneh. Any Lebanese who has been through the civil war can tell you about the "whistle"; that growing strident sound you hear before a mortar shell hits. It still gives me goose bumps. Many are the cases where the whistle is the last thing one hears before meeting their creator.

Puffing my red Marlboro while thinking once and again about quitting smoking, I spot an old dark green Mercedes 180 rushing toward me from the South. As it moves closer toward me, I notice that it's packed with people and its roof loaded with mattresses and luggage. They are fleeing the war zone. It is almost 5:30 a.m.

Three more cars follow minutes apart, rushing at dangerous speeds toward Ashrafieh. Crossing the large open area of the train station is hazardous and, if there's a sniper in the area now, people crossing would be sitting ducks, let alone the shelling gaining in intensity.

5:46 a.m. The radio comes finally to life:

– *Spirou, Spirou, aamaliyet.* (Arabic for "Operation Center")

– *Aamaliyet, Spirou.* I reply immediately.

– *Spirou, aamaliyet, delivery on the way. ETA in a couple of minutes. Coming from the North.*

– *Aamaliyet, Spirou. OK. Standing by.*

I stick my head inside the Clock Tower's hatch where the rest of the team are crouching:

– *Guys, they're coming. Aamaliyet just buzzed. Let's move.*

Everyone exits the Clock Tower and we all stare North looking for the helicopter. This is when we hear the faint flapping. The Augusta Bell Huey rotors' sound is unmistakable, so is its shape.

We all keep staring North waiting for a visual. Then it just appears; flying very low – almost touching the buildings surrounding the Sin El Fil Boulevard, it slows down and gets ready to land. By the time it flies over our heads and toward the landing zone, we can almost reach up and touch it.

Before it even touches down, Mama and Nounours are already pulling out a stretcher from the ambulance while I run toward the helicopter. Sierra starts the ambulance and follows without getting too close to the vortex created by chopper's blades.

The helicopter lands facing South and the two stretcher carriers rush from behind toward the wide-open access door to the right of the craft. I am already there. A soldier sticks his head out and starts waving his arm frantically telling Mama and Nounours to stay away from the tail rotor. I look inside the chopper where three soldiers are watching over a wounded comrade on a military stretcher. The victim is covered with a dark brown wool blanket. The pilot looks at me over his shoulder, while the copilot punches some buttons on the dashboard. Mama and Nounours arrive.

The helicopter noise is deafening. Rotors are still running at full throttle allowing the craft to take off quickly. This creates a vortex of frozen air that hammers and destabilizes us. I could barely remain in place as my overalls are being filled with air. Mama and Nounours are fighting to stand still with the stretcher.

We all quickly salute each other. I stick my head and arms inside the chopper to start transferring the victim onto our stretcher. As Mama rushes to help, the soldier inside stops us abruptly:

– No. Stop. You can't move him, he shouts as loud as he could, his voice muffled by the rotors' noise. *He's badly hit. If you do, he'll die. You have to take him with our stretcher. We'll recuperate it on the next trip.*

I look at Mama then nod at the soldier. I look for Nounours who is standing behind me. Mama and I can't pull the stretcher out alone. Nounours, still holding the ambulance stretcher, drops it on the floor and rushes to help. Sierra is there with the ambulance, around 50 feet away from the chopper. He turns the vehicle 180 degrees with its loading bay facing us and backs it up as close as he could get, jumps out and opens the back doors wide. He then runs toward the ambulance stretcher left by Nounours, picks it, moves it away, and starts helping us carry the heavy helicopter stretcher and victim to the ambulance.

One of the soldiers inside the helicopter waves at the team and shouts:

– A second helicopter is on its way. It should be here in 20 minutes.

I nod and raise a thumb up. We rush the stretcher toward the ambulance while the helicopter lifts off in a tornado of dust and flying debris. Heads down, we start pushing the stretcher inside the belly of the ambulance but... It does not fit! An easy 30 inches are still bulging out! The helicopter wooden stretchers are bigger and bulkier than the Red Cross ambulances. There is no time to reflect on the situation. I immediately shout:

– Sierra, start the car. I'll kneel on the back door's lower plate and hold the stretcher between my knees.

– *What?* says Mama, *are you crazy?*

– *There's no other way,* I reply while climbing up the tray, *the guy is dying. Come on, come on, let's move.*

Without further argument, Sierra starts the ambulance, while Nounours and Mama jump in from the side door. Nounours sits with his back to the driver's cabin and holds firmly the stretcher by the wooden handles. Nounours is big, that's why his call sign is "Nounours", but he has the heart of a baby.

Without hesitation, I kneel on the large aluminum panel that serves as a tray to slide stretchers in. I firmly hold on to the roof's metallic rim of the ambulance with both hands while locking my knees against the stretcher's wooden handles. We rush out of the train station and towards the HDF (Hôtel-Dieu Hospital), 5 minutes away. Sierra is an excellent driver; he can maneuver the narrow Beirut streets easily and yet maintain a relatively high speed.

Most of the way is up a steep hill, and despite Nounours' efforts, the weight of the stretcher and victim are painfully pressing against my knees and thighs.

Mama, ever curious, gently lifts the blanket off the victim's abdomen to assess the extent of the injury to determine whether it requires any immediate intervention. The expression on her face is obvious. Nothing could be done... The poor soldier's intestines are hanging outside his abdomen, and random gauze sheets covering parts of the gaping wound have bonded with the coagulated blood.

Mama places the cover back gently, looks at Nounours and me and hopelessly drops her head down.

We finally reach the HDF's Emergency. The awkward site of the open ambulance and me holding the stretcher between my legs strikes everyone. The ER team rushes to help while I repeat to them exactly what the soldier on the helicopter told us: *"You can't move him; we'll pick up the stretcher later".* My legs are numb and I could barely stand straight. I pick up the radio and call the Operations Center:

– *Aamaliyet, aamaliyet, Spirou.*

– *Spirou, aamaliyet.*

– *Package delivered to HDF, leaving for next delivery.*

– *Affirmative. Report when you reach delivery zone.*

– *Got it, aamaliyet.*

Now we have to drive back to Sin El Fil's Al Abed Clock Tower, hide again, and wait for the next helicopter to arrive.

It is now 6:20 a.m., and the sun is up. The streets remain empty. No one is going to work or schools today. On our way back to the landing zone, we cross a GMC truck with a Katyoucha mounted on it. A militiaman with a bandana holding his long hair and a dark black beard covering his face is tightly holding onto the machine gun while the vehicle speeds towards Karantina. We also come across two more cars packed with passengers and belongings, fleeing the area. We reach the landing zone in less than 7 minutes. We don't have to wait too long this time. As Sierra parks the ambulance behind the Clock Tower, the radio buzzes simultaneously with the arrival of the second helicopter:

– *Spirou, Spirou, Aamaliyet.*

– *Aamaliyet, Spirou.*

– *Spirou, Aamaliyet; second package on the way.*

– Affirmative, we have visual already. Thank you Aamaliyet.

– Spirou, Aamaliyet; good luck guys.

The helicopter is already overhead. Same altitude, same deafening sound, same scenario.

This time, we have to transfer the casualty from the helicopter stretcher to the ambulance's one. Mama tells the crew that we had to leave their previous stretcher at the hospital. The soldier nods. Nounours and I come rushing with the ambulance stretcher that we left behind. Sierra had tucked it under a bush behind the Clock Tower before we left with the first casualty.

The wounded soldier has a bandage covering much of his head, right cheek and lower right neck, where it got thicker and red soaked with blood. A bullet or shrapnel certainly must have hit him. We forgot to ask if the culprit is still lodged in the wound.

The transfer goes by the book; Mama and I hop in the back with the victim, while Nounours takes the passenger seat. Always, only two first-responders sit in the back.

Sitting in the ambulance facing the victim, I start noticing blood sipping out from the bandage, down his neck and onto the stretcher's grey plastic. The poor man is either unconscious or heavily sedated.

In a reflex, I immediately place the palm of my hand over the bandaged area covering the neck wound and press firmly. This creates a pressure point that eventually reduces or stops the bleeding temporarily. I calculate that it should be enough since the drive to the hospital is short.

Deserted roads are ideal for Red Cross missions. It

guarantees getting victims to hospitals within the golden hour. The "golden hour" is a time period that lasts between few minutes to an hour that follows a traumatic injury. During this time, the likelihood of survival and recovery is substantially increased if adequate medical attention and treatment are provided.

We make it to HDF in 9 minutes.

In an orchestrated routine, Sierra stops the ambulance, and informs Operations that destination is reached. Nounours steps out from the passenger seat, opens the side door for Mama, then circles the ambulance and opens the back-bay door to pull out the stretcher. Mama gets out first, and as I get ready to stand up, I start to remove my hand off the victim's wound and freeze still. My palm is glued to the bandage and wound. By the time the blood had stopped flowing due to my pressure point, it coagulated and bonded my hand to the bandage gauze. This is an awkward situation; I can't move.

Mama is watching. She is witty and very sharp, the ideal companion to have in the back of an ambulance. Always lucid and composed, she immediately rushes to the Emergency hall, and returns holding a bottle of Savlon, used in cleaning and disinfecting wounds, and preparing patients for surgical procedures. It is also a powerful blood solvent.

She starts squirting slowly the dark red liquid between my fingers and the wound, carefully trying not spill too much. Nounours and Sierra work on helping me pull off my fingers without jeopardizing the wound or inducing another hemorrhage. It takes 5 long minutes to release me. Unfortunately, the hemorrhage resumes almost immediately due to the mixture of Savlon and lack of pressure. The patient is swiftly transferred to the operating theater.

I am exhausted, and to make things worse, tonight is my shift again at Echo.

(Jad)
THE TALISMAN
1983

That night, I was thinking how once more, the Red Cross volunteers are playing God.

It is now 4:00 a.m.; Boxer and I were busy sorting the casualties and readying them for transfer to Echo. There is a soldier lying on a stretcher, with no apparent wounds. He is pale white and obviously dying. As I get closer, I notice that most of his back is missing. That's why nothing is apparent on the front. The soldier is constantly trying to mumble something that I cannot figure out. From his wounds, I wondered how he is still alive. I get closer to the soldier's face, put my ear against his mouth to attempt to decode what he is trying to say. But I couldn't understand a word. The soldier keeps pointing downwards with his chin, as if he is trying to show me something.

A field doctor approaches, and I explain the situation to him. The doctor looks closer and says:

– *Damn, this guy should be dead. He should be dead by now.*

I was worried and sad that the soldier might be hearing us and about what would be going through his mind...

I kept staring at the poor soldier's lips and face attempting to understand what he was trying to say or point at. Then suddenly, a very unlikely thought strikes me.

– Could it be? No, it can't. It's just a myth... I'm wearing one. I inherited it from my Dad who inherited it from his grandfather...

– What is it? asks the Doctor.

– It's a piece of wood from the Holy Cross.

– The Cross?

– Yes. A talisman, a piece from Jesus' Cross. Few people carry it. It is claimed to protect you from accidental death.

The dying soldier hearing the discussion starts nodding his head vehemently. I reached around his neck and pulled out a thin gold chain. On it is hanging a small round pendant resembling a box and engraved with The Virgin Mary's effigy.

I held it in the palm of my hand and squeezed hard for a while, and looked the soldier in the eye. He was going in and out, grasping for air every 30 seconds or so, with his eyes rolling back and then all of a sudden opened wide. Tears started to burst from his eyes, dripping on the sides of his cheeks, stripping the dust off his skin. The dying man stared back at me and slowly blinked as if he was telling me *"it's all right, you can take it off".*

I stared back at him, this time tears were falling down from my eyes, dripping on my hand holding the pendant. Every memory floated in my head, from the time I remembered my Dad lying in his bed with his face blue and lifeless, to the guy that I first shot in my life, to the injuries I sustained, everything in a slow motion while still staring at the man's eyes rolling back and forth. In a brisk move, I pulled the chain and snapped it off the soldier's neck, while both the doctor and I kept staring at the victim. Ten seconds later, the soldier exhales his last breath...

For a moment, I tried to grasp the absurdity of the situation. I am a believer, but never imagined this is possible. Is it just a coincidence? I started to think what would happen if I was the one dying with the pendant still attached to my neck. Would that person holding it firmly do what I just did? Have I just killed another person that I have to add to my list? Am I a true killer that will never see heaven? I felt the lowest that day! I was angry with God and Jesus....

Dawn is breaking and the fighting is winding down. Fighters on both sides are exhausted and short on ammunition by now. It's cold. When being active, you do not feel the chill. Boxer and I put on our orange coats, our eyes are burning. We have not slept all night and have seen and done things we never imagined we could.

While someone's job is to kill, our job is to save, but here's the contradiction; those who kill do it to save lives, while some of the lives the volunteers save go back to the front, only to kill more...

(Jad)
AT THE MORGUE
1983

My Team 5 co-workers were on shift at Echo. It is a hectic night, mostly busy with *"Chocolats"*, dead, rather than wounded soldiers. This means the morgue is witnessing the heaviest traffic.

Abou George is in charge of the morgue. He is the master of the dead.

Abou George is a celebrity at Echo. He is huge – 6 feet 3 inches tall, as much wide, and over 275 pounds; with abundant grey hair and long thick mustaches rolled up in an endless spiral. His face is inflicted with a permanent frown that intimidates everyone. No one dares to speak to him.

Yet, Abou George has a heart of gold as large as his waist. All that heart goes to the soldiers, the dead ones. At the morgue, he treats the martyrs with such reverence and respect, it borders on veneration. His job is to wash and clean the bodies of the dead soldiers, dress them in a new uniform, wrap them with the Lebanese Flag, and tag them to be delivered to their families. Some were so mutilated; the tag was the only mean of identification.

At 11:00 p.m. Mama and I were helping Abou George at the morgue. Red Cross volunteers managed to nurture a close relationship with him. They are helpful, kind, and respectful. Bodies fill the morgue floor, some very badly mutilated. I kneel next to a corpse; a large gaping wound in the neck was visible. Coagulated blood that turned black obstructs the full view of the damage. His head was barely still attached to his body. I call Mama:

– *Mama, can you please hand me a pair of scissors?*

Mama reaches for a stainless-steel table in the corner, on which Abou George keeps some of his surgical tools, and hands me a sharp pair of surgical scissors, not really knowing why.

Wearing gloves, I put my left hand under the remaining part of the soldier's neck, and with the other, hold the scissors get ready to cut the remaining artery and skin that is holding the head to the body. At that moment, Mama almost loses it, starts crying and shouting at me with a hiss:

– *No, No, Jad. You can't do that; you don't have the right to do that... it's not right.*

She rushes out of the morgue crying; I lifted my head and looked at her! I had an empty look! I was not realizing what I was doing. Those were the orders we were given after all, however, not everyone might or could have carried them. Maybe I was by now so immune to this kind of situations, that it has become a second nature for me. Any loose body part, you remove and tag. I finished severing the head and tried lifting it, but it was very slippery; I gently pulled it by the hair, getting ready to put it on a white cloth and wrap it. All of a sudden, the electricity goes off.

Usually, I do not panic in a similar situation... This time was different. The circumstances, the place, and what I had in my hands... all of that played differently. I start running around in the dark looking for the door, still holding the dead soldier's head by his hair and screaming but with no audible voice coming out of my mouth. A very weird and strange sensation! Instinctively, after realizing that I was still holding the head of the poor soldier, I let go of the head and started running toward where I assumed the door was located. I stumble, and almost fall, my right foot landing in what feels, and sounds like a bucket filled with water. Reluctantly, I stop. I realize that, if I keep panicking, I will surely walk over other corpses and probably fall.

I hold back my fear, close my eyes and start breathing calmly. In what seemed an eternity, generators kicked off and the power takes a minute to be restored. The lights in the morgue flickered and the fluorescent strips lit up. I look around me to assess my situation.

I am standing less than an inch from another corpse, my right foot is in a bucket filled with blood and not water, and I am panting heavily. In a reflex, I pull my foot from the bucket and run toward the front door where Mama was standing, her face white like milk, and terrified.

– *Jad! Oh My God! Are you ok? I'm sorry. I'm sorry. I panicked. I'm sorry. I know I should not have! But it was much more than I could handle! It was surreal. I am very sorry.*

– *It's ok. I understand. I'm pretty shaken too*, I reply.

Abou George comes in, looks at me, puts his large palm on my shoulder and tells me with the hint of a smile:

– *It's ok. You did great. I know of doctors and even soldiers who would have had a heart attack had they been in your place. I was there too habibi, I am used to it happening and I still feel butterflies in my guts when it happens, the only bad thing is that you will always dream of what took place tonight, you will never forget it nor get used to it. That's the worst part of what happened to you tonight, my son. I'm much older than you, I have been doing this for a much longer time that you have, and I still wake up in the middle of the night screaming and sweating. I am very sorry you had to experience something like that at a very young age.*

It was the first time that I realized that Abou George was indeed a human being and not a mean robot.

(Eby)
A REAL ER
1983

Boss, Kebbeh, Mama, Shorty, Skinny, and I are on shift tonight at Echo. The story of Jad and Mama at the morgue is still making the headlines at the military hospital and 102. While some talk about it with reverence, others get a kick out of it.

It is 8:45 p.m., and a fresh batch of casualties just arrived in an M113. We hear a tank's roaring engine increase from afar. It enters the narrow Emergency access and comes to a sudden halt under the main door's canopy. As it stops abruptly, the armored troop carrier swings back and forth while smoke from the engine and brakes fill the air with a distinctive stench; a mixture of rubber, burnt oil, and fuel. Its long radio antenna caresses the ER canopy, drawing a long black streak.

We are assigned a room contiguous to the main Emergency corridor, allowing us to respond immediately. Inside the small space, we stacked foam mattresses, supplies and equipment, radio chargers, and a duffle bag containing biscuits, bottled water, and snacks. We are cramped in there, but that's the best we can get. We are lucky; room availability is quite scarce these days at Echo.

We all rush out. Military Emergency medics are already out helping to evacuate the tank.

I possess an over-excited character, Jad does too. The

difference is that I am emotional while Jad is more rational. Although we both react in the same manner, I worry less about the consequences. Jad is a charismatic born leader, I am not. He has a *"je ne sais quoi"* that makes him a natural hero. I have to admit that people are attracted to leaders and heroes more than the emotional, subdued type of guys. I figured that out after years of doubt and drowning myself into dark and gloomy ideas, thinking that I will never achieve anything in life. I realize now that achievement is a reward you give yourself instead of expecting others to give it to you.

We reach the hatch of the tank as it starts to open and we freeze. Blood is dripping abundantly between the hinges of the bottom seam.

The massive steel door flips down slowly, and then hits loudly the concrete floor, splattering blood everywhere. Inside the tank, as my eyes get used to the darkness, I notice four seated soldiers and three bodies stacked on the floor. The front-most seated soldier to my left has his right thigh wrapped in bandages, and blood seeping out. Facing him is another soldier with his M16 on his lap. He is huge and had to bend his head to fit in the tank. His chest is so large that the anti-shrapnel vest he is wearing would not buckle up.

One of the Emergency doctors, an officer, wakes everyone up from their lethargy, including me:

– *Come on People! Let's get to work.*

He then looks at us, and orders:

– *You take care of the bodies; we'll handle the wounded.*

I do not want to take care of the dead. I am not a mortician, but can I argue with a high-ranking army officer? Everyone scrambles to work. Boss and Kebbeh start prepping the corpses inside the tank while Mama and Shorty go inside the ER to get stretchers.

They can give all the orders they want; I decided to help with the wounded, and that was it. Let them sue me! Boss gives me that famous look of his that says *"Eby, instructions, follow the instructions".*

– *I'm fed up with playing mortician. I want to play Medic. Damn it!* I replied to his silent warning.

– *Ok, ok, fine!* he replies lowering his voice and looking around to see if anyone is listening.

I am curious by nature. My curiosity is geared toward knowledge and science. I am fascinated with science fiction, astronomy, medicine, and arts. It is my hobby and most of what I do during my free time. I want to look at these poor soldiers; I want to see the wounds up close. I have always been amazed by their power of endurance. I never told anyone, but I am scared to death by war and fighting. My nightmare is to find myself on the front with a gun. People argue about my fear when they know that I am with the Red Cross. As a matter of fact, I specifically joined the Red Cross to avoid getting drafted by the Christian militias. It is not the same, not at all. Carrying a gun is not like carrying a stretcher. I respect Jad a lot for having had the guts to fight. Although I could never grasp the underlying emotions associated with this type of adrenaline rush, I still respect my brother for being at the front at such a young age. Maybe I should not, maybe he (like many others) were just instinctively submitting themselves to that adrenaline rush; maybe it was never the "cause", but rather the urge that made him and others carry a gun, point at the neck of another human being, and shoot to kill. I now realize that it takes so much, so many breeds of people, to make a world. Jad and I are from two different breeds, but with one ultimate goal, and my fear of losing him comes from my nightmares of losing my own life. No matter how wars are fought, the most powerful weapon is the human psyche. That's where you win, and that's where you can lose.

The "big" soldier jumps off the tank and starts walking toward the Emergency main entrance. His sleeves are rolled up all the way to his shoulders. His biceps are the size of my thighs. A machine gun encircled by a crown of thorns is tattooed on his left arm with the words "For God and Country" in Arabic. As I look at him, I wonder what's wrong with him. He does not seem wounded or even under shock. Maybe he is an officer, I think to myself, who decided to escort his company.

As he enters the ER and steps into the white neon-flooded corridor, I notice a hole in his anti-shrapnel vest, on his lower back left side. Yellow Kevlar fibers are bulging out from the 2-inches opening. He must be wounded, badly. For anything to pierce this type of vests so brutally, it must have reached deep.

– *Let me help you take that vest off,* I say while walking toward him with a smile, dwarfed by his massive stature.

– *I'm fine!* barks the soldier with a deep baritone voice and a threatening frown. *I can take it off myself, but I'm fine.*

– *No, you're not. Look at this hole. Does it burn or hurt?*

– *No. It did not reach the skin.*

– *Let me check. Please take off your vest.*

At that point, the soldier throws a look at me that clearly

says "*You lay off or I will seriously hurt you*". Intimidated, I stop and take a slow step back just as one of the Emergency doctors approaches us. He sees the gaping hole in the soldier's vest.

– *Take off that jacket now. This is an order.*

Most doctors are, luckily, officers. Reluctantly, the soldier starts taking off his ammunition belts and then the vest. He mumbles that he is fine and that nothing is wrong with him, while looking at me with eyes that could shoot napalm. Deep inside, I am hoping he is wounded for good, because if he's not, I'm likely to be the one ending up with a wound.

The bullet-proof vest finally comes off as the mumbling continues. Underneath it, matching the location of the gap; his military camouflage shirt had another hole blackened with blood.

– *The shirt. Step in there and take the shirt off now,* orders the doctor, pointing at Room 3.

I follow the soldier into Room 3. More mumbling as the shirt comes off.

– *Fuck!* I hiss. I could not hold it.

Right above the belt line, the soldier has a 2.5-inch hole on his side. I can see the flesh inside and the burnt skin around the wound. There is no blood, which indicates that whatever caused this wound must still be lodged inside obstructing the vein and blood flow.

What shocks me the most is that the mastodon looks like he does not feel a thing. I am amazed by the legendary endurance of these guys. I keep hearing stories that sounded more like myths. This is the first time I witness it firsthand.

– *Nurse,* the doctor shouts. *Help him take all his clothes off and prep him for surgery.*

– *Surgery? What surgery? I have to go back to the front!* Shouts the soldier. *Can't you give me a couple of Aspirins and a Band-Aid for the wound? I'm fine.*

The doctor is absolutely not in the mood for arguments after a 14-hour straight shift.

– *You shut the fuck up, take your clothes off and lie on the fucking bed! Am I clear soldier?*

– *Fine,* mutters the huge guy finally complying.

– *Can I help?* I ask once more insistently, really craving to see how the surgery would proceed.

– *No, not here. They might need you in Room 2,* answers the doctor without even looking at me.

I am skinny and I weigh 130 pounds. Although tall enough, I do not possess a stature to impress. My orange overalls look oversized and my thin face and glasses bestow on me the look of a nerd rather than a macho. That makes me invisible, and people who don't know me often talk to me without looking at me... Even some who knew me well did...

I head for ER Room 2 joined by Shorty who was next to me all the time. There is the other soldier, the one with the bandaged thigh. He is lying on the operating table with his pants off, and now the wound is clearly visible. A 5-inch-long and 1.5-inch-wide slit in the skin. Inside the wound darkened by the trauma, the muscle could be seen contracting and relaxing every time the soldier moved his leg. He is sedated and can barely feel the pain by now. The doctor prepares the suturing tools while the male nurse applies sterilized sheets of blue green cloth around the wound and cleans it profusely with Savlon and gauze.

Holding the needle, the doctor lowers his head and looks at me over his narrow reading glasses.

– *Wanna give it a shot?*

– *A shot? A shot at what?* I answer with a puzzled and rather nerdy look.

– *Stitching! You want to help me suture the wound?*

– *Me? Now? Yeah. I mean No! Wait... I've never done that before!*

– *You're Red Cross, no? They don't teach you how?*

– *Umm, no actually.*

– *Good. Wanna learn? This is your chance. It's easy.*

– *... Ok. Yeah, why not?*

– *Put a mask and gloves on.*

You see? This is the over-excited me, emotionally jumping on an opportunity without heeding the consequences. I am not sure whether I am ready for this or not. In any case, it is too late to change my mind. That doctor seems cool and willing to teach me; this is probably my only chance. I head to the aluminum cupboards behind me, pick clean scrubs, a pair of blue rubber gloves and a mask and put them on.

– *You're not keeping that cap on your head. Are you?* says the doctor with a smile, *Get him a bonnet!*

As a proud first-responder, I always wear my black beret with the golden Red Cross insignia pin on it. I'm blushing now.

The doctor asks me to stand close to him while he starts piercing the skin with the long, curved needle to apply the first suture. I watch closely as he explains how to hold the needle with the scissors in the left hand, pass it through the skin and to the other end of the wound, while twisting the thread in a knot with his right. This is not your average type of knot, and I can't keep up with surgeon's dexterity at tying the complex knot.

After two sutures, the doctor passes the scissors and needle to me.

– Now you try.

Sweating and shaking a little, I start gently pushing the needle in the skin around the wound.

– Harder. You have to push harder. The skin is hard. And stop looking at me. Watch the wound.

Ok, here's another secret; I hate needles. I despise needles. What I despise the most is seeing them pierce the skin. I can easily take the pain of a needle stuck in my arm, but I can never look at it going in. Now, I had to suture a huge wound. That is not funny.

Probably by now, you are starting to wonder what I am doing at the Red Cross with my needle phobia and fear of war and emotions... don't ask me, I don't know either. All I know is that I simply love every second of it and would not give it up for the all the gold of the world.

The nurse must have noticed the abundant sweat beads running down my forehead, onto my eyebrows, and dripping on my glasses. He moves in and starts tapping my forehead with gauze. How cool is that? I used to watch M*A*S*H on TV and now I am acting it. I cannot help smiling generously under my mask.

For the first suture knot, I have to be guided by the surgeon. Every suture goes better and smoother than the previous one. I apply four more sutures before I decide to stop. Anxiety, the feeling of responsibility, and precision of work exhaust me. My hands are shaking. Now I have far more respect for the medics who perform such procedures for hours, and sometimes days, nonstop.

– *I have to stop. Boy! How can you guys do this for hours?* I ask.

– *Habit,* answers the doctor. *Habit.*

– *Thank you so much. I'm overwhelmed,* I reply while lowering my mask and smiling.

I then approach the heavily sedated but lucid soldier:

– *You'll be fine. I added glue to every stitch,* I say with a smile, later realizing how cheesy that was.

The soldier replies with a faded smile and slow nod. I take off the surgical gloves, throw them in the collector bin at the entrance of ER Room 2 and head to our resting quarters. I was still shaking and my legs felt like jelly. Shorty gives me a tap on the shoulder.

Not all nights are busy at Echo, and that makes everyone happy, not because we get to rest; but because it is a sign of fewer casualties among the soldiers. As for the rest, if Abou George sleeps well, no one else can.

The corridors of Echo are famous, and everyone one jokes about how "Echo" earned its call sign. On calm nights, if you whisper at one end of the long corridor, you can be heard very clearly on the other end. That is fine, until Abou

George goes to sleep. I have heard people snore before, but not like Abou George. It is more of a roar mixed with the shriek of a dying bull with a slit throat. The rumbling and thundery snorting echoes across the corridors leaving everyone awake and trying to devise ways to stop the torture.

No one dares waking Abou George up or even closing the door of his room. So, most of the nights at Echo you can hear him snore at one end of the corridor, while we all whistle in tandem at the other end, in a vain try to make it stop. Weirdly enough, it sometimes works. Although I never understood the science behind it, I keep whistling until we could finally fall asleep and earn ourselves an hour of rest.

(Jad)
CPR... AT ANY COST
1983

Of all the training and rehearsals, the most important is CPR. The Red Cross rookies are subjected to intensive drills, practicing mouth-to-mouth resuscitation techniques on test dummies built for this purpose. The dummies can provide immediate feedback on whether the technique is efficient or not. Inaccurately delivered, CPR can either be without any effect or, at worst, kill the patient. Detecting the vitals of a patient is equally important; applying CPR to someone still breathing and whose heart is still beating can be fatal.

Everyone at 102 still remembers the grueling training days, the numerous failures, and finally the first success. As a famous French saying goes "*Le malheur des uns fait le bonheur des autres*", which translates to "The misfortune of some, is the wealth of others", and so, each fresh 102 graduate aspires to his or her first CPR and to provide the kiss of life. But theory is always rosy...

On that mild and sunny morning, we are stationed at the Antonines School in Baabda. Located in the eastern suburbs of Beirut, Baabda is where the Presidential Palace is situated. To reach it, you have to pass by a Syrian checkpoint that harasses drivers and occupants, asking for IDs, frisking passengers, and searching vehicles. They seldom gave ambulances any hard time. The Baabda Antonines School is to the right, a mile after the checkpoint.

It is built on a large property and features one of the largest sporting complexes in the country. Most of the Scouts Jamborees are held there.

Every year, a major sporting event takes place with different disciplines ranging from marathons to gymnastics. Athletes from the Middle East, the Gulf, and North Africa flock to compete.

The Red Cross is always present at such events in case an athlete collapses or the public needs help. With the hot and sunny weather, dehydration is common.

I parked the ambulance under a tree near the running track and I sat in the shade with the rest of the team, on the open back tray and enjoyed a first-row seat to the show. During similar events, the day usually goes very smoothly and, for the first-responders, it's a perfect occasion to relax.

From where we sit, we have an unobstructed view of the track, including the Start line. I can see the athletes warm up and take position on the white line. I hear the umpire's gunfire signaling the start of the 2 miles endurance race. Two minutes later the athletes' pack zooms past the ambulance. Starting the next lap, they will disperse and run much slower.

After the third lap, I stood up and started walking around the ambulance to stretch my muscles. I had my back to the track when the team heard people scream from the opposite side. I walked closer to the edge of the track, held my palm on my forehead to shield my eyes from the sun, and squinted trying to see what the fuss was all about. I could see people gathering on the track. I knew something was wrong. I called the rest of the team and started running across the track to the other side. They got the first aid bag from the ambulance and followed.

I reached the side of the track facing the public podium. People are standing up trying to have a clearer look at the events. On the floor, between the running lanes, a tall black man in running jersey and shorts is lying still on the floor. Around him, other athletes and event officials are gathered. One of them is kneeling next to the victim sprinkling water on his face, and gently slapping him on the cheek. As I arrived, the crowd made way. I knelt next to the victim. On his jersey, is printed "Ethiopia", along with his native country flag. He is huge, at least 6 feet tall, covered with sweat and without any signs of life.

I shout, asking if he can hear me. I was trained to ask three times. I check his pulse at the wrist, the thigh, and then the neck; nothing. I bent over the man's face and placed my ear next to his mouth trying to pick up the sound of breathing or feel the air exhaled. Still nothing. Clearly, the only thing left is CPR.

– *Take the chest, I'll take the mouth,* I said looking at Joura.

First-responders always try to avoid the mouth, especially when the victim is old or from the same gender... I knew there was no time to argue.

Joura knelt, looked for the edge of the sternum above the abdomen, placed the bottom of his left palm on it, and then his right palm on top. He locked his elbows to avoid bending and got ready. I lifted the victim's neck with my left hand to keep the esophagus clear, closed the nostrils with my right fingers, and opened his mouth wide. I took a deep breath, tightly locked my lips against the victim's, and blew.

The victim's chest rose under Joura's palms. This is the sign. Joura pushes down as hard as he can and starts counting.

– *1001, 1002, 1003, 1004, 1005...*

After five pumps, I blew again. We repeated the maneuver for four times, still nothing. On the fifth round, Joura pumped the heart; I bent and, as my lips touched the victim's mouth, the athlete gaged and threw up, sending vomit straight into my mouth. I pulled back violently and started coughing and spitting while everyone was looking perplexed.

Joura stood up and ran after me. With a sign of my hand, I asked him to remain with the awaking victim. I ran across the field to the ambulance and profusely washed my mouth and face with water. The taste and stench were unbearable, so I did the unthinkable. I took a bottle of pure surgical alcohol, filled my mouth and gargled for few seconds, overcoming the burning sensation. I spat the liquid with a loud shriek and washed my face. I stayed in the ambulance waiting for Joura and the others who showed up minutes later carrying the giant athlete on a stretcher. They transferred the patient to the nearby Baabda hospital, where I was given a preventive shot.

Back at 102, the story made the Center's headlines. I could even tell what the athlete had for lunch. Everyone was having violent convulsions of disgust as I insisted on letting my fellows relive the moment by telling my story over and over and with accurate details.

It all ultimately ended with a good laugh, but not for me. From then on, the smell or even remote thought of vomit makes me feel sick.

(Jad)
A GIFT OF LIFE...
1983

Apart from the reckless behavior, the adrenaline rush that the 102 first-responders get from saving a life is the true reward. Nothing gets even close to the ecstasy of successfully achieving a mission and knowing that a life was saved.

The Red Cross enjoyed complete respect and admiration from the majority of the Lebanese population, independently from all petty considerations. Many are the times when 102 gets a knock on the door and a cake, sweets, even money are delivered as tokens of appreciation from the saved victims or their families. All gifts are returned with a big "thank you". We never do what we do for gifts. Our job description is clear: to give, and never take anything in return. Stories, tombstones, and epitaphs stand as clear witness to that creed.

The gift of life did mean something even more intense to me. Delivering a baby was never in the Red Cross manual. Volunteers were never trained to give birth.

The early 80s were tough years in Lebanon. The civil war is at its apogee. Shelling starts without any warning, battles rage for days, and lulls are scarce. Rushing to shelters is now a perfectly orchestrated maneuver. The Lebanese know exactly what to do. Pack food and water, candles, flashlights, spare batteries, a radio transistor, blankets, and (most importantly) cigarettes. But they do not always manage to be fully prepared... not when a pregnant woman is in labor.

On a pleasant September 1983 afternoon, Gazelle and I are doing a routine shelter tour in Gemmayzeh. 102 does often that during heavy war days. We deliver water, Panadol (aspirin) pills, and occasionally food to stranded citizens. The ambulance drives around the Center's neighborhood West of Gouraud Street, East to Sursock, and North toward Fassouh and Sassine Square. We make the tour in pairs, not the usual four volunteers per ambulance.

I was driving the 176 loaded with six packs of "Sohat" bottled water, large bags filled with Panadol pills, and a couple of cartons of Klim powdered milk.

I drove down the 102's street, and reached Gouraud facing the Holy Heart School, my school. I made a right turn and headed toward Accaoui. Our first stop is to the left, less than half a mile away. I reached the building and parked the ambulance next to Eterna, the only watch repair shop in Gemmayzeh. The owner is Armenian and has been running the business since the early 70s. He is known in the neighborhood for his grumpy character and stiff face that never smiles.

Gazelle jumped out of the 176 first. We slide the side door open and carried what we could, before coming back for a second round. The shelling was intensifying on the front a mile and a half away from where we were standing. We could hear the shells fall closer and the unmistakable sound of AK-47 machine guns.

We ran to the building entrance facing the ambulance and rushed down the stairs exiting the lobby, toward the shelter two floors below. No one takes the elevators anymore in Beirut, at least not for less than two or three floors. Getting stuck in an elevator can earn you a solitary night in the elevator car.

– *Damn man! I hope we can make it back to 102,* says Gazelle.

– *You bet your ass we will,* I replied. *I'm not spending the night in a shelter with a bunch of geriatrics!*

– *Unless a couple of hot babes are stuck there too.*

– *Hum... Then I might start getting scared of bombs,* I answered with a loud laugh.

We received a heroes' welcome in the shelter; it was always the case. The elderly shower the volunteers with prayers and good wishes, and the youngsters stare at them as if they just saw Batman walk in the room.

We put the supplies in one corner of the shelter and ask if anyone needed medicine. While doing so, we heard a long moan followed by a loud scream. We turned towards a darker side of the shelter. There, a woman was sitting on the floor with her back against a man's chest. She was pregnant, and he must be her husband. An older woman, probably her mother, was also talking to her. As Gazelle and I approached them, we could clearly see the woman's large belly.

– *Fuck!* I whispered, *she's going into labor.*

– *Yes, she is, and from the sounds we're hearing, she looks like she's gonna have her baby here and now,* answered Gazelle with reference to the intensifying shelling.

Shells are falling much closer now, so close that we could hear the infamous long whistle preceding the touchdown.

We knelt next to the couple and tried to evaluate the situation. The woman's contractions seemed to be getting closer to each other.

Gazelle ran to the ambulance and returned with the blood pressure gauge, oxygen, a stretcher, and an extra blanket. I had already radioed 102 for instructions. I was told to stay put, the situation was too critical to drive around with a pregnant woman in the back of the ambulance. It seemed that Ashrafieh was being heavily shelled.

There was a first-responder at 102 whose cousin is an obstetrics specialist; Operations would call him and ask for precise instructions.

Meanwhile, we attend to the woman in pain. We provided her with oxygen to ease the pain and regulate her breathing. She was 29 years old and carrying her first baby. She got married 2 years ago and settled in Gemmayzeh. I tried keeping her busy while monitoring her contractions. That was the only thing I knew about delivering babies, the contractions. I remembered watching a TV show where a woman was about to deliver, and the doctors and nurses around her kept talking about the contractions and how the time interval between them is an indication of the imminent birth.

Suddenly, the woman screamed and fell back on her husband's lap. I saw a liquid gushing from between her legs. The blanket covered only her belly and thighs. Her water just broke. The baby was coming out, now.

Gazelle and I were in a state of panic and trying hard not to show it when, like a voice from Heaven, the radio came to life. 102 informed us that we would have to perform the delivery in the shelter. They spoke to the doctor and he agreed to guide us step by step through the radio.

After I gave the doctor a brief on the situation, he agreed that there is no way the woman could be transferred to a hospital anymore. Gazelle and I looked at each other with a mixture of fear and thrill.

Gazelle rushed back to the ambulance to get the necessary gear; surgical gloves, sterile gauze, etc. By the time he was back, the woman's contractions were so close to each other they almost became continuous. She was in a lot of pain.

I was already prepping her following the doctor's instructions over the radio. He asked her husband to sit right behind her so she could lean against him in a half-seated position. Her legs were wide open and folded up as far as they could go against her large belly.

The doctor then asked me to help her breathe, exhaling as intensely as she could, and then pushing with all the force she could muster. He insisted that I should update him on the extent of the dilation.

Gazelle created a perimeter around the couple and the woman's mother, and asked everyone to sit on the other side of the shelter and give the mother-to-be some space and privacy. Even as they tried to be helpful, everyone was actually impeding the effort. Gazelle gave me surgical gloves and wore a pair himself. He pulled a sterile grey bed sheet from its sealed wrap and placed it under the patient, then stood above me and holding a torch. All we could do now is wait and hope the mother-to-be did the necessary effort. She was obviously exhausted from all the fear, sleepless nights, and runs to shelters.

The doctor clearly instructed us not to do anything except help the woman breathe and push. And that's exactly what we did.

The husband was obviously in shock. While watching to see the baby's head appear, I asked the husband:

– *This is the first time you witnessed a delivery, right?*

– *Yes. I never imagined it's that hard on a woman. Is she going to be all right?*

– *Of course she is! Both my brother and I were born through caesarean procedures,* I said smiling.

– *I wish I could do that,* the woman replied between two breaths.

We laughed, which softened the pressure on everyone, mostly me.

– *Now you have to push as hard as you can, it's almost dinner time,* I say with a smile.

The woman looked at her husband laying his hand on her forehead and gently caressing her while nodding with a smile. The woman arched forward and with a loud scream pushed as hard as she could. I held the hand of Gazelle carrying the torch and pulled it closer toward the woman and looked:

– *Yes! I can see the head. Keep pushing. Keep pushing. It's almost over.*

I took the radio and pressed the talk button:

– *102, Champ. Tell the Doc I can see the head. What is the next step?*

– *Champ, 102. Standby.*

A few seconds later:

– Champ, 102. The doctor says she has to keep pushing as hard as she can. Once the head is out, she cannot stop, the pressure around the baby's neck will asphyxiate it. You will have to hold the head on either side by placing your hands around the neck under its cheeks. Do not pull, I repeat, "DO NOT" pull, just hold it straight over.

– 102, Champ. Got it. Meanwhile, ask the doctor what I should do once the baby is fully out.

I switched my attention back to the woman. Tears were falling abundantly on her face and she was in excruciating pain.

– I'm sorry but you have to keep pushing. You cannot stop.

Then I remembered, and turned toward the husband:

– I don't know her name, I said with a funny face.

– Caroline, answered the husband, looking at her tenderly, *Caroline. And I am Jihad.*

– Ok, Caroline, push now. Come on. What are you wishing for? A boy or a girl?

– Anything. It doesn't matter. Just let the pain end. Boy, girl, all is good. And she screamed and started pushing again.

The head was halfway out now. Gazelle focused the light between the woman's legs. We could clearly see the forehead, eyes, and a part of the nose. I begged her to push harder.

In a herculean effort, Caroline pushed as hard as she

could, and the rest of the head popped out and fell into my hands.

– *Come on, Caro,* said the mother. *Come on my love, the head is out. It's almost over.*

The father looked over his wife's body, trying to see the baby's head.

– *We're done, babe. One last push; we're finished.*

From the look on her face, I had serious doubts about whether Caroline could deliver that one last effort. But I underestimated the power a woman, a mother, can harness. Caroline, in one last scream, her face twisted beyond recognition by pain, pushed so hard, the baby's body slid out in a snap, followed by the umbilical cord. I was still carrying the head as instructed. Now the newborn was lying on the sterile bed sheet still.

– *Buzz 102, Gazelle. Check on the next step.*

While Gazelle contacted 102, I remembered the movies again. I held the baby by the feet, turned him upside down and gently tapped on its the lower back a couple of time. The baby started crying immediately.

Jihad and Caroline were both looking silently at me.

– *It's a boy.*

The whole shelter burst in cheers, laughs and applause. They could not keep silent anymore. The suspense was unbearable.

– *You have to cut the umbilical cord,* shouts Gazelle.

– *What? Cut it?*

I did not think about that. For me, it was over already.

– You have to clamp it on the baby's side and cut it. Here, I'll do it.

Gazelle reached for the first-aid kit, pulled a pair of clamps and another pair of sharp scissors. He did what he was asked to do, and wrapped the baby in another sheet of sterile cloth and placed him on his mother's chest.

We radioed 102, announcing the success of the operation. We were instructed to wait for some time and then carry the mother and newborn to Geitaoui hospital. A lull was starting to reign over Beirut.

Our adventure rippled across 102 and other Red Cross Centers around the country. We were nicknamed the Doctors, and naturally, all kinds of jokes (funny and sick) started pouring in. But that mission yielded more than jokes and congratulations.

There are times where you do what you do every day, only the outcome is different. In a country plagued by death, being gifted with the bliss to see life in the making shines a ray of hope on the darkness of despair.

es secouristes de la Croix-Rouge à la recherche des victimes
i les ruines.

"The day little Pascale was found under the rubble, L'Orient-le-Jour newspaper was there to capture the harrowing moment. I am in the foreground of the picture carrying the stretcher."

(Jad)
THE ONE-MAN OUTPOST
1983

I was at work early that Tuesday. My uncle's clothing shop is less than 2 minutes away from home on foot, but on the upper parallel street. The night before was "busy". The sporadic shelling and fighting went on until dawn on the Green Line splitting Beirut. The neighborhood suffered a couple of hits, but luckily no one was hurt.

That morning I was busy unloading a fresh stock of wool pullovers and women's nightgowns from a minivan, when a loud explosion rocked the neighborhood. I froze and dropped the box I was carrying. I looked left and right for smoke. Gemmayzeh is a long narrow stretch. I could oversee the whole street, from the Sacred Heart School to Accaoui Street, just by looking left or right from where I was standing. There is no smoke, yet the explosion sounded very close... I immediately thought that it must be on the lower side... Where I lived...

I then saw people rushing down the connecting street a few feet to the right of the shop. That narrow street joined the upper Gemmayzeh to the lower Pasteur Street, where my home is located. They were shouting:

– Oh my God. Oh my God. Poor people, it fell right next to the gas station...

Unconsciously, I shifted into Red Cross mode, dropped the box on the floor and started running toward the explosion site. My uncle standing at the door shop yelled:

*– Hey! Where do you think you're going? We have work
to do here! Come back. Come back now!*

But I was not listening anymore. I had already reached
the top of the connecting street, just next to the "Comet
Taxi" office whose owner is climbing on the hood of his
vintage Rambler to overlook the explosion site. I was
wearing brand new trousers and shoes that I purchased for
a very good deal the day before from a shop in Ashrafieh,
one of my uncle's clients.

I always kept my Red Cross badge and bib on me. My
badge always hung on the inside of my shirt and the bib was
folded in a small square into my pocket. While running, I
pulled the bib, wore it, took my badge from under my shirt
and hung it on my shirt's pocket.

The gas station was less than 400 feet from where I
lived. I was glad, filled with guilt, but glad.

I rushed toward the clerk standing there and clearly
shaken. I asked where the phone was. The clerk pointed
at the small office at the back of the station. Before going
there, I looked to my left, into the narrow alley that
stretched from the carwash down to a cul-de-sac. Smoke
was everywhere and rubble filled the patio.

I ran into the station office, lifted the grease-stained
phone while praying to get a dial tone and a connection.
During the war, both happening simultaneously was a pure
miracle, except for a few privileged that had "connections".
Usually, most gas stations were very well connected. I
dialed the Center and got Castor on the line. I asked him to
bring an ambulance and join me immediately, hung up, and
ran toward the explosion site.

Among the rubble and smoke of the typical Beirut vintage building, a woman was being held back by neighbors. They were standing in front of a room on the ground floor apartment. There were no outer walls and the interiors were exposed to the patio now. She was hysterically shouting:

– *Pascale! Pascale! My daughter Pascale was sitting there, right there.*

She was pointing at the gaping hole with both her hands and trying to free herself from the people holding her back.

– *Leave me alone! Let me go! Pascale... Pascale...*

– *Where?* I asked.

– *There. There. She was playing on the floor near the TV.*

I rushed inside the room. It was very dusty and the smell of gunpowder was overwhelming. It looked like a living room. Half of a TV was protruding from the rubble. It was an old set with a dark wood casing and knobs on the right side. The screen was shattered. Then came the shock. I noticed a small hand lying on the top of the TV with the index finger pointing outward and other fingers folded in. At first, it looked like a part of a doll. As I got closer, I thought that it looked strangely realistic for a doll hand. I knelt and looked closer. The hand was not attached to an arm, or a body. It was just resting there, alone.

I stopped for a moment staring at the little hand. That must be Pascale. It couldn't be anyone else. Damn.

At this moment, Castor entered the room. I did not even hear the ambulance siren. I was startled by the voice of Castor asking me about the situation.

– *Get a black bag from the ambulance,* I order while still

staring at the little hand.

We always carried black plastic bags in the ambulance. Similar to garbage bags but thicker; we used them to collect body parts of deceased victims.

Castor disappeared for a minute and returned with the bag. I was already carrying the severed hand. Castor opened the bag and I pushed my arm to the bottom and placed the little hand inside. *"I can't just throw it in,"* I said to myself. Castor put the bag on the floor and then, we both turned our heads in opposite directions, looking for more remains. I noticed that Castor was a little shaken.

While we continued scouring the debris, I noticed a long lock of black hair covered with dust protruding from the rubble. I held it and gently pulled back. I wanted to make sure it is not just hair. As I kept pulling, a head came out of the rubble without any resistance... Just a head. No body. It was the head of a girl with long black hair. The face was mutilated and covered with thick dust. I kept holding the head by the hair, turn toward the bag and slowly placed it inside.

Castor was a couple of feet away watching! He suddenly leaned over with one hand on the shattered TV set and started vomiting. I stood there looking at him for a while and thinking: *"Man! Some of us are so hardened and emotionless by now and some others will never get used to it"*. I did not know which of those I was, the hardened or emotionless, or simply confused by the horrible scene.

– *Hey! Take it easy buddy,"* I said. *"We have to keep searching.*

Castor nodded without raising his head or looking at me. He stood there for a while, then wiped his mouth with the back of his shirt sleeve and went back to work.

We recovered a leg and the thorax of Pascale. The rest of her body was never found. We gathered the limbs in the bag, put them on the stretcher, covered the whole with a blanket and prepared to exit to the ambulance. I took the front of the stretcher. My new trousers were soiled and the new shoes totally damaged.

We walked carefully over the rubble heading towards the exit. The smoke had lifted. Luckily, Pascale's mom had been taken away to a neighbor's house. No mother is supposed to see her child carried out in pieces in a black plastic bag. Just as we stepped outside the room and onto the street, a journalist with a camera snapped a shot. He was from the "L'Orient-Le Jour", a French speaking newspaper. We were featured on the first page the next day. How sad!

I still have the Red Cross bib I was wearing that day and the press cutting of that shot.

On that infamous day, only Pascale, the 7 years old girl died.

That particular day and this particular mission never left my memory! Every time I am saddened by a life happening, Pascale comes to mind. To this very day, I still hear the cries of her mother resonating in my ears.

I am now jokingly referred to as 102's one-man outpost of my neighborhood. Most of the accidents that happen in and around my work in Gemmayzeh see me first on site. It always is the perfect escape from work.

On another Monday, it is not different. I heard a detonation. I rushed out of the shop and looked left and right as usual. Nothing. No smoke or rubble. Just like the last time when the little Pascale was killed, I once more saw people hurtling down the street that connects upper and lower Gemmayzeh.

– *Damn it! Not again,* I said to myself, and I started running.

My uncle does not spare me the usual "we have work" talk. As I reached the end of the connecting street, I stopped and looked around me. I saw the heavy smoke, and this time it was coming from the North, right where our home is. A million thoughts rushed through my head as I raced toward the blast.

Before I reached my destination, I could already see the heavy smoke filling the air right under our building and in front of the main entrance. My first reaction was to look up at our apartment on the fifth floor. Mom was standing on the balcony, alive. That's all I needed to know. Now I could focus on the explosion site.

Our building was located on the only wide stretch of the whole street. To my left, a couple of cars were severely damaged, but they did not seem to have any passengers. To the right, people were gathering, gesturing, and shouting in front of Elie's car upholstery shop. Elie, an Armenian, and his son Pierre have had that shop ever since we moved in to the building, back in 1970. I reached the crowd and started pushing them aside. I had already my bib and badge on, so the onlookers let me through. In front of the sidewalk lied the mutilated body of a man. Blood was everywhere, and shards of glass and rubble covered the sidewalk and the few cars parked nearby. I knelt over the body to check for vital signs, unfortunately there were none.

I asked to cover the corpse and told Pierre to try and call 102. All that was available to cover the body were old

Armenian newspapers. Meanwhile, my Mom was shouting from the fifth floor, begging me to take cover. It was quite a frequent occurrence for a second shell to hit the same spot. It was a tactic used to make shelling more precise, by relying on feedback from the first shell, usually through listening to the Red Cross, Civil Defense, or the enemy's radio channels, and obviously inflict more human losses.

Next to Elie's shop was a very old and small house with its basement serving as a muffler-repair shop. It was owned by Jack, another Armenian. He was hurt by the blast and I had to attend to him while waiting for the ambulance.

Once help arrived, I went up home, grabbed a copious meal, and took a small nap before returning to the job I hated.

After all, and despite the pain caused to others, it was a normal Monday!

(Eby)
CHEATING DEATH
1984

Cheating death is routine at 102. Almost every mission has a brush with it. Some are mild, while some others are so close; we all wonder how we manage to make it back alive every time.

In summer 1984, I have been engaged to Aline for 3 months now. My wife-to-be and I are determined to make it alive to the wedding day.

Delta has been closed down now for almost a year and 102 is reunited again. Not because the war has winded down, but circulating between the regions of the Center's jurisdiction has loosened.

The radio buzzes. Bobob is on shift that early afternoon. An ambulance needs to be dispatched to Sioufi to perform a hospital transfer, which means moving patients from one hospital to another. This is very common during the war.

There is another war going on, a hidden one, the Hospital War.

Hospitals in Lebanon are notorious for refusing to admit patients if they cannot afford paying for admission fees, however serious their case is. Corruption plagued every institution, and humanitarian services were not spared. The dysfunctional government is either helpless or manned by politicians who benefit from the situation.

The Red Cross repudiates this outrageous behavior, and volunteers tried many times to expose it, sending letters to Operations and the Higher Council. Nothing has been done for years, until early 1984, when hospitals were finally forced to accept anyone in Emergency. If they couldn't, they had to keep the patients inside the Emergency and attend to them, until they arrange for an alternate hospital willing to admit them; hence the frequent hospital transfer missions.

Boss and I played an important role in bringing this decree to fruition. We both once drove a badly injured old man, whose house was hit by a mortar, to the Emergency of a Hospital in Ashrafieh. We had to leave him at the Emergency entrance after transferring him onto a hospital stretcher, because we were immediately called to another mission, assuming the ER crew would take care of the victim. Our next mission was also redirected to the same hospital. We arrived there only to find out that the poor man was still lying on the same stretcher in the corridor of the Emergency ward and had bled to death. No one has even checked on him. The hospital's argument was that none of his relatives showed up, and they were too busy! This is when we raised our voice and immediately called Operations begging for something to be done. A week later, the famous decision was made by what was then left of the government and generalized among all hospitals.

102 has just received new state of the art Volvo ambulances. Perfectly equipped, with a powerful engine and automatic gearboxes, they are much more silent and comfortable than the usual Volkswagen Transporter (although, at 102, we have an emotional attachment with the Transporters).

Eiffel, Mama, Bobob, and I take one of the new Volvos, which inherited the number 176 from the old Transporter, and head to Sioufi for the hospital transfer mission. The ambulance is parked at the entrance of the street leading down to 102, on Tabaris Square right under the trees. From there, we could drive straight north through Sursock Street and then take a right toward Accaoui road, leading up to Sassine and then down to Sioufi. Ashrafieh is located on a hill. Eiffel is driving.

We drive through the beautiful Sursock Street, where the richest and oldest families of Beirut live. The road is adorned on both sides by old mansions and vintage Lebanese estates, and hosts the famous Sursock museum. Sycamore trees as old as Beirut line the entire street, casting an eternal shade and letting through the thick leaves small rays of light that look like spotlights highlighting the intricate arabesque designs of the mansions.

As we reach the end of the street, Eiffel prepares to make a right turn toward Accaoui when the radio comes to life. It's Kebbeh:

– *176, 176, 102, stop. Possible change of mission. Standby.*

– *102, 176, positive. Standing by.* I answer.

Eiffel prepares to park the ambulance near the sidewalk when, seconds later, the radio buzzes again:

– *176, 102, clear to carry on. Other mission handled by 101.*

– *102, 176, ok, positive. Thanks.*

– *176, 102, good luck.*

Eiffel pulls down the shift stick to Drive and gets moving. As the ambulance clears the turn and heads straight up on Accaoui Street, an 80 mm mortar shell falls 250 feet in front of us. Eiffel instinctively hits the brake with both feet, sending everyone toward the front of the ambulance. Shrapnel falls on the ambulance like a hail shower, and black smoke rushes toward us blinding the view for a few seconds.

Everyone is panting heavily. No one says a word, and then we look at each other, and break in a hysterical and nervous laugh.

We realized that it would have taken the ambulance exactly 10 seconds to be right where the shell had fallen. Kebbeh has just saved our lives when he made us wait those, now incredibly precious, 10 seconds.

Eiffel takes his foot off the brake and we carry on with our mission, driving over the hole caused by the mortar.

Cheating death is not always induced by hazard. We reach a point where conning our own destiny turns more into a game of Russian roulette. The zeal of achieving a mission or saving a life makes us oblivious of our own safety. What is, for some, their worst nightmare becomes an addictive adrenaline rush to first-responders and fighters. Every soldier at war knows how this rush feels like. Reality becomes so distorted that we think we are immune to injury and death; even worse, we are convinced we could cheat it, and always win. Jad and Shorty know very well how this feels like.

On a calm evening at home, Jad and I are sitting on our beds chatting. This is the story he told me.

The ambulance is rushing down the Jounieh-Beirut highway around 11:00 a.m. Jad is driving with Shorty next to him. They were on their way to deliver blood for an urgent transfusion in Tripoli as they were the only available ambulance with the only available couple of AB+ blood pints. They reach a stretch of Jounieh highway that narrows down to two lanes and where traffic jams are a daily event even amidst the war. Driving at a very slow pace, Jad starts getting impatient. He tries to swirl between the cars, honks, switches his turret lights and sirens on, but nothing works. He knows that the cars in front of him cannot go anywhere. Even if they could, they would never do it. It is a typical trait of Lebanese arrogance and lack of empathy toward issues like that.

Few yards before they reach the tunnel Jad has had it:

– *Fuck it. Hang on!*

– *Huh?* says Shorty. *What do you mean hang on? Why?*

It is too late for Shorty to get a verbal answer. Instead, he witnesses first hand why Jad said what he said. He swirls abruptly the ambulance to the left, climbs over the wide dirt divider of the highway. The ambulance shakes violently as it climbs over the concrete lining of the divider, the large chunks of dried soil, and then down the other side. The 176, a brand new, fully fitted Volvo given to the Red Cross by Anthony Abraham, a multi-millionaire Lebanese migrant and philanthropist living in Miami, Florida, is now zooming on the wrong side of the highway at 80 mph, racing toward the Nahr EL Kalb one-way tunnel.

– *Oh my God! Oh my God!* goes Shorty. *This is it. We're gonna die. Fuck Jad!*

Jad is not listening. He makes his way to the extreme right of the tunnel, trying to gain a farther view of the road and see incoming traffic. The traffic from Jounieh is almost nonexistent, Jad is thinking, when headlights appear at the other end of the tunnel and blind him. Now Shorty is screaming with a very high-pitched sound.

The driver in the other car must be a damn good one. At the very last second, he manages to make a sharp turn, avoiding the ambulance by a fraction of an inch. Still going at 80 mph, Jad exits the tunnel, keeps to the right for another half mile, and then, once traffic eases on the opposite lane, climbs once more on the divider, this time getting back to the right side of the highway.

Shorty is now sitting so low his bottom almost touches the floor and the seatbelt squeezes his right ear. Jad manages to swerve between cars, drives all the way to the right side of the road, climbs the ambulance on the dirt shoulder, and speeds toward Tripoli leaving a thick trail of sandy dust and dozens of drivers inventing new insults to express their anger.

The warrior at rest. An undated photo of bozo at 102.

(Jad)
BOZO MADE EVERYONE CRY
1984

Toni, call sign Bozo, was now Sector Chief at 102. He was young, active, sharp, and had a clear sense of leadership. Bozo was a Team 5 member, my team.

He was appointed to head 102 2 months ago and had big plans to bring drastic changes that would save more lives and provide the 102 first-responders with better equipment. For around 6 months now, he and Bomba were in love. She also was in Team 5. Rumor had it they were serious and considering future plans.

It all started a year ago. Bozo and Bomba simply clicked. They tried to keep it a secret in the beginning, but at 102 secrets were impossible to keep. No one really minded, although the usual gossip did spread between teams. Team 5 provided total support to the couple, while in other teams some resented the idea, and some other teams took umbrage and started calling them the "Chef" and "Cheftaine" in French. Time and friendship always managed to fix things at 102, and they perfectly did.

102 did witness its fair share of relationships and breakups. Most of the volunteers were from the same neighborhood; some even went to the same school together. Spirou (Eby), Boss, Gazelle, Shorty, Bouboule, and many others went to the Sacred Heart School, located just at the end of the 102 street in Gemmayzeh; so did I. In fact, Shorty and I were classmates in first grade. They also were Scouts in the same sector, Beirut 7th, they hung out together in Gemmayzeh, and now they met again at 102. A solid cultural and societal bond brought most of the 102 volunteers together. It took a short while for the out-of-neighborhood "intruders" to blend in; but once they did, they quickly became family.

War, hard times, desperation, and near-death missions all contributed to bringing the guys and girls closer to each other. It was natural for intergender relationships to develop into closer ties. The average age at 102 was 22, the age where emotions bloom, when young men and women should be holding hands, kissing, and exchanging love songs. In Lebanon, none of these things were part of the daily routine; they were dreams.

After a very tough month, Beirut was cruising through a period of calm. The dynamics of politics were beyond anyone's comprehension, including most of the politicians. No one really understood why the battles raged one day, only to come to a complete stop on the next. In all cases, it always was a relief. Schools and businesses reopened their doors, and so did shops. 102 and other Centers took advantage to reorganize their supplies, and the volunteers go back to their regular universities and job schedules.

Tabaris Square was located almost on the battlefront. The roads leading into it from the East and South were hazardous, while the ones from the West and North were relatively safe because they were narrower and lined with tall buildings that provided cover from snipers.

102 was located halfway down the narrow street that led west from Tabaris down to Gemmayzeh. It was so narrow that when cars parked on both sides, drivers had to maneuver in a space of less than 8 feet wide.

At the entrance of the 102 street from the Tabaris roundabout and to the left corner was "Chahine au Carrefour", one of the oldest bookshops and home accessories outlets in Beirut. Made up of a ground floor and a basement connected by wooden stairs, it was visited by the Ashrafieh upper class. During the civil war it managed to stay open, and business was good.

To the right of "Chahine au Carrefour", there was a small two story building and then the back alley that led to 102.

It is Friday, January 20 at 11:00 a.m. on a sunny winter morning. Although Beirut was busy studying and working, the activity was barely noticeable around Tabaris Square. In the polarized city, Tabaris was located on the dividing line.

A man rushed to 102 from the back alley shouting and gesturing:

– *Chahine au Carrefour is on fire!*

Bozo, Bomba, Joura, and Gazelle, among others were on shift. They all race out toward the shop. Heavy smoke was already coming out from the wide-open glass doors and the fans vents. The owner, Mr. Chahine was standing outside helpless.

– *Did you call the Fire Department or Civil Defense?* asked Bozo.

– *I tried but cannot get through, answers the disoriented man.*

– *Joura! Go to 102 and make the call. Gazelle, Bomba, go get equipment, ropes and gas masks*, orders Bozo.

Then, looking back at the owner:

– *Is there anyone trapped inside?*

– *I don't know. I had a couple of customers. I don't know if they left?*

– *Where were they?*

– *One was on the ground level and the other down below shopping for books.*

– *Are you sure you did not see any of them stay or leave?* insists Bozo.

– *I don't know! I don't know!* the man answers hysterically. *My God, this is all I have. Please get the Fire Department. Please.*

– *We're calling them.*

Gazelle and Bomba returned with gas masks, oxygen tanks, a thick rope, and first aid equipment, while Bozo was trying to get inside the shop. The black smoke was too thick and toxic now. He pulled back.

– *Did you reach the Fire Department or Civil Defense?*

– *Yes,* answered Bomba, *they're on their way. Joura is online with them.*

– *Good. Give me a gas mask and a radio,* says Bozo.

– *What? No!* shouts Gazelle. *You're not. Are you crazy?*

– *We can't wait. There might be someone dying down there now.*

The gas masks in use by the Red Cross were not meant for fire and smoke prevention. They were only equipped with special filters that let air through, but not smells or contaminants. Volunteers always complained that the masks were not even good at that.

Bozo put on a gas mask and a helmet, took a heavy-duty flashlight, and walked inside the shop.

– *Toni. Please don't,* begs Bomba.

– *Don't worry babe, I'll be back in a minute,* replies Bozo in a cavernous voice from behind the mask. *We'll stay in touch, he says, waving with the radio.*

As he disappeared in the black smoke, Gazelle and Joura looked at each other. Joura had just gotten back from the Center after being assured that the firefighters were on their way.

– He's crazy, says Joura, *we shouldn't have let him.*

It was the last time Bozo was seen alive.

The firefighters and Civil Defense finally made it, and found Bomba, Gazelle, and Joura standing in front of the burning shop shouting as loud as they could, calling Bozo in vain. They tried to no avail reaching him on the radio.

Between heavy coughs, his last barely audible words on the radio were:

– I can't find the way out. The smoke is too thick, too thick.

The firefighters put on their specialized gear and dived in the black cloud of smoke. They emerged 6 minutes later carrying the motionless body of Bozo. His orange overalls were charred, but his skin seemed mostly intact.

They laid him on a stretcher already brought from a 102 ambulance. Bomba, Gazelle, and Joura rushed to give him CPR. They removed the mask. His face and the interior of the mask were filled with white foam oozing from Bozo's nostrils and mouth. His eyes were half shut. His empty stare, dilated pupils, and lack of breathing were clear signs of the inevitable.

Bomba broke out in tears hysterically calling his name. Joura and Gazelle started providing CPR after wiping clean his mouth and nose. It was a surreal scene. The fire raging, the firefighters running in and out of the shop and around the truck, the owner standing motionless, the neighborhood watching...

Everything was moving at an incredible pace, except Bozo and his three comrades. For them, the moment was frozen. Time had stopped. There was nothing they could do anymore. Bozo was transferred to the Hôtel-Dieu Hospital morgue where he was officially pronounced dead.

As the head of 102, Tony's funeral was organized by the Red Cross. Most of the Lebanese Red Cross first-responders were present. Bickfaya, his hometown, was tinted in orange – everyone and everything was dressed in orange in honor of Tony and the color of the Red Cross overalls. Hundreds of volunteers arrived, carried the casket, marched in silence, and attended the service. Ambulance sirens blended with the tolls of church bells and car horns. It felt more like a wedding.

All the first-responders took turns carrying the casket to its final resting place. That day they all cried like they never cried before. Those who "proudly" never cried, like Joura, shed burning tears.

Eby and I were there too. I was in Team 5, Bozo's team. We both walked inside the tomb, where Eby fell on his knees leaning his head against the cold stone and cried abundantly. He knew deep in his heart that this was the first time he cried like that. He felt the guilt of not crying at all when our Father died. Maybe it was his way to repent now, to offer to his Dad the tears he deserved 12 years ago. I heard him whisper:

– *Tony, tell Dad I love him and miss him so very much.*

No one was in the shop at the time of the fire. The two customers the owner referred to had already left... Bozo's life was lost in vain.

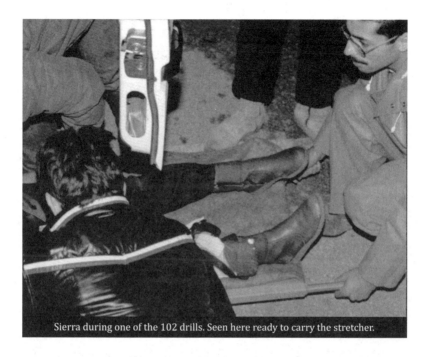

Sierra during one of the 102 drills. Seen here ready to carry the stretcher.

(Eby)
SIERRA, THE SILENT WARRIOR
1984

There is one unsung hero at 102, and he was in Team 1, my team. Selim, call sign Sierra, was calm, silent, and polite. Although not the most popular guy, he was the most helpful person in the team. His nerdy looks, lack of sense of humor, and shyness made him quite misunderstood and rejected. He was always there when needed, yet never here.

Sierra lived close to 102, just toward the end of the street that leads from Tabaris Square to Sursock. That made him among the first to arrive at the Center in case of emergency.

He was an American University of Beirut (AUB) engineering student and, from what everyone heard, a bright one. By his looks and thick glasses, one could assume he invested most of his time into studies. AUB being located in West Beirut, Sierra had to cross to the East side every day to return home. The crossing was quite hazardous at times. He had to go through Syrian, Muslim, and then Christian militias barrages. Sometimes, snipers decided to practice their hobbies in the early afternoon when the crossing gets busy, and without any prior warning. Yet, Sierra made it every time.

1984 was a "busy" year for the rescue services in the Lebanese Civil War. 102 was in full swing and the mission's pace was increasing at an alarming rate. Even the blood bank was often running out of supply.

University students are heading toward the end of the spring semester and working hard to prepare for their end of term exams. Studying and researching in times of war is not easy. Pupils have to deal with the stress of both studies and war.

The dream of going to university kept igniting my passion until I grew up. Today, I teach branding and marketing at one of the leading universities in Lebanon, and every time I go there and look at my students I take a trip back in time and become 20 again. God was kind enough to bless me with this consolation prize and I am so grateful.

Electricity is scarce during the war and students face endless nights studying by the eye-straining light of candles or propane camping lights. To make things worse, during heavy shelling nights they have to squeeze in shelters with dozens of neighbors and deal with the noise and distractions. Yet, somehow, they always manage to make it. Sierra was going through this right now, trying to earn his engineering bachelor's degree.

It was another endless night of heavy shelling and fighting and Beirut residents remain in shelters that morning. Buildings are ablaze and streets are littered with debris, burning cars, mortar and RPG tail fins, and broken glass. Some of the narrow streets of Ashrafieh are completely obstructed with rubble.

This is the story of Sierra as told to me by Nounours on that ominous day when I came running all the way from home to 102.

It was Monday, February 6, 1984. Sierra has been stuck at AUB since last night. He could not make it back home and managed to sleep at a fellow student's dorm on the campus grounds. With him is Nounours, who is also a student at AUB.

At 10:00 a.m. that morning, a lull flooded Beirut in an utter and eerie silence, only interrupted by an occasional fleeing car's exhaust rumble. Even ambulances do not use their sirens. They don't need to. After hearing news that the passage between West and East Beirut is about to be closed, Sierra and Nounours decide to make a dash home. Sierra thought that if they walked up to Spears Street, where 101 and the Lebanese Red Cross headquarters are located, and then from there under the infamous "Ring" bridge, they would make it to Tabaris. Then they could head to 102 and he could finally go home, few feet away. Nounours lived in a building facing 102, just across the street. The plan sounded good.

Sierra has with him two classmates, German sisters who live in Hazmieh, on the outskirts of Beirut. The girls had no mean of communication to put their panicking parents' mind at rest. The last time they spoke was yesterday in the early afternoon, according to a 101 staff.

Sierra, the helpful and nice guy, proposes to bring the girls along with him to 102 where they were guaranteed to reach their parents. The Red Cross had some of the few remaining operational phone lines in Beirut. The sisters agree to go.

Sierra, Nounours, and the two sisters leave the campus at 10:15 a.m., walk up toward Hamra Street and then North toward Spears. They reach 101, where Sierra and Nounours identify themselves and ask for a status report on the situation. They are told that the very fragile lull is not holding anymore. The shelling is resuming and increasing in intensity, and that the crossing is about to be closed soon. The sisters try to call their parents but fail to reach them. Phones working at 101 do not necessarily mean they are on the recipient's side... So, Sierra contacts 102 on the radio and informs them about their plan. He asks the girls if they still want to join him. They are determined to make it home. They all wait for another 10 minutes, and then leave 101 toward the "Ring" intersection, a walk that takes less than 1 minute. They were accompanied by a 101 staff who walks with them up to the intersection.

At the intersection, Sierra, Nounours, and the girls hide behind the wall of the corner building. They look left and right to make sure the road is clear. On that intersection, to the left is the notorious Murr Tower, an unfinished 40-story reinforced concrete skyscraper. Started just a year before the war, it was about to become the tallest building in the Middle East. Now, it is a Syrian stronghold from which snipers located on the top floors can overlook, and reach, most of Beirut. The tower is the most dreaded structure in Beirut. Aside from snipers, the empty windowless floors are used as torture chambers and to incarcerate abducted citizens. Stories are abundant.

All seems calm. If they make it past the open field of the intersection, they would reach the mile-long "Ring" overpass, go under it, and walk home, relatively protected by the concrete ceiling of the bridge.

Sierra looks at the girls and Nounours, and with a rare smile says:

– *This is it. We cross the intersection, go right along the wall over there, and then under the "Ring". Are you ready?*

Everyone acquiesced. Not that they had many choices left by now.

– *1, 2, 3, let's go!* shouts Sierra.

They cross to the other side of Spears, run through the intersection, reach the wall next to the bridge, and dash to the other side, right under the "Ring", where they vanish. They are now surrounded by the no-man's land on either side, with only a narrow passage that gets them safely to the opposite side of Beirut.

Twenty minutes later, they make it to Tabaris and go straight to 102. The shelling is intensifying at an alarming pace. The German sisters are anxious to go home. Nounours thinks it is wise to contact 106, the Hazmieh Red Cross Center, and check on the situation. Hazmieh is close to

Baabda where the Presidential Palace and the Ministry of Defense are located. It is also on the way to Souk El Gharb. Hazmieh is at the crossroad of one of the hottest fronts in the civil war; the Chiah - Ain El Remmaneh frontline, and is a target of choice for shelling. It overlooks the southern suburbs of Beirut. Nounours is told that going there now is highly not recommended. He informs the two sisters who still refuse to heed his warnings. Finally, trying to calm them down, they all decide to walk with Sierra to his home, where the girls can try to call their parents and inform them that they are staying safely at 102. Once the situation calms down, the girls will be driven home in an ambulance. The "reliable" phone lines are not working at 102 this morning, and Sierra, ever helpful, thought his home phone might be operational.

Shorty is on the lookout outside the back alley that leads from 102. He rushes back and tells everyone that the shelling is intensifying alarmingly, but the girls still would not change their minds. Sierra and the sisters leave 102.

A few minutes pass, less than 2... The incoming whistle of a shell, a deafening explosion, the sound of shrapnel and debris raining on car roofs and the asphalt, a spine-chilling scream, then utter silence.

Nounours freezes. Shorty, still at the alley door rushes out. He returns immediately:

– *God! Oh my God! Don't go out. Don't go out and look.*

Macho and Blondy, from Teams 2 and 5, are on a second lookout at the opposite corner, facing "Chahine au Carrefour", where Bozo died 17 days ago. Macho saw Sierra and the girls leave the back alley, cross the narrow street and walk toward Sierra's home, 500 feet away. The mortar fell when the three of them were less than half the way. Startled, Macho and Blondy instinctively jump inside the shop and hide. They wait for a few but endless seconds, then they both rush out and run toward the smoke.

They reach the still smoldering crater, just as another first-responder arrives and shouts at a man trying to drive his car away from the fire, asking him to run and hide. It is too late for Sierra. The mortar pulverized his body, and what is left of him is barely recognizable. One of the German sisters is also immediately killed by the blast, while the other does not make it to hospital.

I am home working on my model kits, my only hobby. I love to build tanks and jet planes. In a routine procedure, I call 102 to inquire about the latest developments and to ask if I am needed. It is then that Joura informs me. I hang up and leave home running for 102. On the way, a million ideas rush through my head. God! It could have been Jad, or me. And Sierra... Poor Sierra.

I reach 102 as a team is getting ready to leave and inform Sierra's family. As for the German girls, we had to call AUB to identify them and later inform their families. Sierra's funeral is set for the day after tomorrow.

There is nothing left to do. We spend the evening and most of the night at 102 in silence. Later at night, I leave for home and fail to sleep a single minute. I stay up all night on the balcony smoking. Death keeps creeping closer. When is my turn?

With the breaking of dawn on the next day, the shelling and fighting resume and intensify. Anyone who could make it to 102 shows up as early as possible. They are very few, along with the team on shift since last night. I arrive there at 7:00 a.m. It is decided that those from Sierra's team will be at the funeral, while everyone else stays at 102, knowing that missions would be abundant and to minimize risks.

The next morning, arrangements are made for Boss, Kebbeh, Mama, and me to take an ambulance to the morgue, place Sierra's remains in a casket, and drive to St. Demitrios Orthodox Church, commonly known as "Mar Mitr" ("Mar" is the Arabic equivalent of Saint) where the family and Eiffel, Shorty, and Boxer would be waiting. As the ambulance reaches the morgue, hell breaks loose. Heavy artillery slams the Ashrafieh neighborhoods at the rate of one mortar every ten seconds.

We make it to the church, less than a mile away, but only to find out that Sierra's family did not. The shelling is concentrated on the area now. The priest decides to start the service with those present, fearing for his own life. We object at first. How can we start the funeral service of Sierra without his family? But we have to reluctantly comply as the battle rages in a constant crescendo, and explosions get closer.

Halfway through the service, the shelling intensifies to a point where the priest starts reciting the prayers and chants at a very fast pace, while anxiously looking up at the roof of the church. With every shell that falls everyone ducks instinctively, while dust falls off the windows and walls of the decades-old holy place.

The service ends in half the usual time, cut short by the priest. He looks at us with fear in his eyes and shakes his head sideways regretfully indicating that he could not carry on. Sierra's family still did not make it. Now we have to carry the casket to the cemetery located within the church's vicinity. The St. Demitrios cemetery is one of the largest in Beirut and its Carrara marble tombstones and shrines the lushest. Some of the richest aristocrat families of Beirut are buried there like the Bustros, Sursock, and Tueni. Behind the church, there are two-story high walls with 3 feet by 3 feet square metal doors covering small burial chambers where the middle-class Beirutis Orthodox are buried.

The pall bearers walk down the small alley behind the church, preceded by the priest and two horrified young choirboys carrying candles and a large cross. I can't help wondering how their parents allowed them to go out on a day like that. The Priest and choirboys accelerate their pace as we try to keep up carrying the heavy casket.

Shells are falling very close now, and with every blast everyone walks faster. The priest is almost running now, and ahead of the choirboys. Suddenly, an 82-caliber mortar falls right behind the procession, almost at the entrance of the church. For the priest and the choirboys that is the warning call from the Almighty. He turns toward us with a regretful look. He does not say a word. He just turns back and runs for cover, leaving behind him a trail of incense smoke from his thurible. The two choirboys follow, one of them dropping his candlestick while the other holds the tall silver-plated cross like a spear in one hand and raising his white robe above the waist with the other to run faster.

We just stand there alone and disoriented.

– *We have to move guys. Come on; let's find the tomb!* says Boss.

Our procession resumes, but it is now more of a race. Boss and Boxer are ahead looking for one single open metal door in the huge endless wall. Boss thinks that the undertaker must have opened it already; he is right. The small square door is located on the second row up toward the end of the wall. Someone has already written in Arabic calligraphic letters with a marker on a small copper plate, Sierra's full name, and year of birth and death, and riveted it on the white square door.

We rush and shove the casket in the hole, shut the door, and close the padlock already hanging open on the hinge. Then, under the heavy shelling, we all gather around the tomb, and said a prayer. No one is crying, but sadness fills the air. I pick some yellow wild daisies growing between the wall bricks and place them in the padlock hinge, and we all run for our lives back to 102. The ambulance is covered with dust and gravel from the mortar that fell earlier at the church entrance.

It is already enough of a torture for parents to see their children leave home every day not knowing if they will ever come back. Not being able to attend your child's funeral is a punishment no mother or father deserves. Sierra's mother is still waiting for him to come to supper.

As for us at 102, we realize how much of a void Sierra left. After the death of Bozo 2 weeks ago, I can never get over the idea of losing someone I was with in an ambulance few days earlier, someone I was talking to face to face, someone who was so close I could smell his sweat. Sierra is a hero, a silent warrior whose voice can be heard now, even louder than when he was alive.

(Eby)
ANTENNAE AND SNIPERS
1984

The abandoned construction site behind 102 was supposed to become a modern high-rise in Beirut. After erecting the skeleton of the 15-story building, work had to be halted. Real estate in Lebanon is not quite the hype these days; the location of the building is too close to the front line which divides Beirut into East and West, leaving a big question mark on the future of the area. What's more, the height of the construction makes it dangerously exposed to sniper and mortar attacks.

It is a massive structure aimed at Beirut's elite. Each floor is to house one flat. The terraces and balconies have an unobstructed view of the Port of Beirut and the Mediterranean to the West and the Sannine Mountains, Jounieh bay, and as far as Byblos to the North.

The south side of the building faces West Beirut and houses the stairs and elevator shafts. Since the building is still mostly a skeleton and has no walls, the stairs, as of the seventh floor, become exposed to snipers located in the infamous Murr Tower on the West side of the Capital. To make things worse, there are no rails or handles, and one false step would send one in a free fall to the ground.

This building stands witness to Sierra's death. It faces the site where he fell with his two German university colleagues.

But 102 has no other alternative. The structure is the perfect location for the center's vital communications antennae and other aerials. It has a 360º clearance, ideal for uninterrupted and clear reception of radio signals. 102 technicians have installed UHF and VHF antennae, a TV aerial, and a small power generator to feed the attached equipment. Running a power cable this far and this high is not impossible, but power cuts were so frequent and lengthy that an independent generator was indispensable, let alone snipers and shrapnel likely to severe a power cable.

The generator runs 24/7 and has to be constantly fed with fuel and have its oil changed. This entails climbing up the 30 flights of stairs carrying fuel-laden jerricans. This is the easy scenario, and it seldom occurred. The more realistic scenario entails "running" up the 350 steps carrying 20-liter jerricans and performing a balancing act right in the middle of the stairs. Too much to the right and you could fall down the stairwell; too much to the left and it's the street below. To spice things up, snipers fancy playing "hit the duck" with our orange overalls, and on heavy fighting days mortars whistle past us. At 102, this is business as usual.

It is Thursday afternoon and I am on shift. I had just arrived to 102 after a long boring day at work. Business is scarce; I am working as an Art Director at an advertising agency on Sin El Fil's highway. We had just enough clients to pay the salaries. A logo here, a small advertising there, and occasionally a crazy client willing to pay for a TV commercial keep us busy enough to barely fill the 8-hour shift. On good days, it takes me 20 minutes to get from work to 102; but on busy days, traffic is unbearable, and I have to spend 45 minutes to cross the 5 miles.

It is a relatively calm day. When I say "relatively", I mean compared to the day before. So far, we've apparently had only one blood transport mission to Hôtel-Dieu Hospital. Once I reach 102, I notice on the task sheet pinned to the corkboard over the radio set that it is time to fill the communication equipment's generator tank. Eiffel is manning the radio shift.

– *Hey! Wanna go up fill the generator's tank? You and I need the exercise with all the smoking we do!* I say jokingly to Eiffel.

– *Yeah, sure why not?* he answers while sipping on his red Marlboro.

So, Eiffel and I volunteer. I have not done it before and I want to see what the view looks like from up there. Eiffel and I agree to rotate the jerrican carrying every two floors, hoping to make it to the roof before the nicotine in our lungs gives us a heart attack.

We walk through the back alley that connects 102 to Tabaris Square, head left toward the building, and reach the construction site surrounded by crumbling and rusty fences. Most of the heavy-duty mesh fences are still holding to steel poles, but since Sierra's demise, those poles are bulging toward the inside and the mesh fences have been blown away well into the intended building lobby by the mortar shell that killed him on the opposite side of the street, the crater still gaping and filled with sewer water. It is a reminder of that infamous afternoon, a few weeks ago. We can't help pausing for a second and looking at the sidewalk as if Sierra's body is still lying there.

We walk inside what is supposed to be the lobby, then left toward the staircase and start the tiresome climb. The first six floors are relatively easy. We climb slowly and take breaks between floors while exchanging the jerrican. All we have to worry about is the fall. As we reach the seventh floor, the rules change. Now we have to climb as fast as we can and we cannot stop, except after every first flight of stairs – every floor had two – and even then, we had to keep our head down.

We stop at the seventh floor to catch our breath. We crack some jokes about giving the finger to the snipers on the other side of the Green Line and resume the ordeal, climbing two stairs at a time and swinging the heavy jerrican from one to the other. At the end of every set of stairs, we have to make a quick 180º sharp turn to take on the other set. This was where it gets the most hazardous. If I slip and lose my grip, it's the big dive.

We make it to the 11th floor and things look good. We can hear intermittent explosions and machine gun bursts coming from the front. Eiffel hands over the jerrican to me as we start climbing the 12th floor stairs. We turn to start the second flight of stairs, and I stop. I am exhausted and short of breath. For Eiffel and me, cigarettes and stairs don't go well together, and boy! What wouldn't I do for a cigarette now? I duck on the small slab splitting the two flights of stairs followed by Eiffel. From there, we are facing snipers, while on the first flight we had our back at them. Either way, the bullet is lethal, but with you looking the other way it provides a fake psychological sense of safety.

We get ready to take on the last steps toward floor 12. I look at Eiffel; pass the jerrican to him and dash up. Eiffel follows as quickly as he could. As my head pops above the steps and West Beirut dawns, two strident whistles startle me, immediately followed by two thumps and smoke. Eiffel freezes as he reaches me out of breath.

– *Come back! Come back!* he shouts, as he runs down the stairs and ducks, placing his head as low as he can behind the jerrican.

I immediately follow while looking for the bullets impact. One has hit the wall to the left of my head and ricocheted to the other side falling in the shaft. The second bullet has hit to the right of Eiffel on one of the stairs steps of the second flight.

– *Fuck! That was close,* I whisper as if the sniper could hear me. *The bastard has been following us trying to go for a kill shot! Now what?*

– *We stay here for a while and wait,* answers Eiffel. *Radio the Center.*

– *But we can't stay here forever, if we go up or down, we're sitting ducks.*

– *These assholes are playing,* whispers Eiffel. *It's not personal,* he continues with a grin. *After a while, they'll get bored waiting for you and shift to an easier target. We just have to be patient.*

I radio the Center and speak to Boss, informing him of the situation. He concurs with our recommendation to stay put and asks me to radio him every 5 minutes or once we're on the move again.

This is the perfect time to light up the cigarette I was craving for. Eiffel forgot his pack at the Center and asks for one. We both lie on the floor with our heads on the first step and wait. I take a puff fervently and, while exhaling the smoke in loops, think about how funny the situation is, and this possibly being my last smoke.

– *Do you think it's a good idea to smoke?* asks Eiffel.

– *Huh?! What? You're seriously worried about my health now?* I answer sarcastically. *I'm touched!*

He laughs.

– *Actually*, he replies, *without even looking at me, I'm worried about mine... If the motherfucker is still aiming at us and sees the smoke or light, it's like waving at him with both arms...* Then Eiffel turned slowly his head and stares at me.

– *Fuck!* I whisper as I throw my cigarette butt on the floor and start rubbing it with my sole.

Eiffel has already extinguished his. We wait for another 15 endless minutes, and then I say:

– *Ok. We've gotta to do something. Going down is stupid. We're almost there. So, if we're to take a risk, I say we take it up, and now.*

– *You're right*, agrees Eiffel, *then we'll worry about the way down.*

– *Besides, it's starting to get dark and the jerk wouldn't want to strain his precious eyesight.*

– *Let's keep a gap between each other. It's better... You know what I mean?* says Eiffel. *If one of us is hit, the other can still call for help.*

– *Yeah you're right, I'll go first.* I answer. *I'll radio the Center and tell them we're on the move again.*

I radio Boss again informing him of our decision, pick the jerrican, run up the stairs without waiting for Eiffel, and go through the remaining four floors reaching the roof. I exit the stairs, and immediately duck against the half-height wall that circles the perimeter and let myself fall completely out of breath. I do not check on Eiffel at all. But I did not hear any bullet whistles either. Eiffel appears just a few seconds later. We crawl to the left and toward the west end of the roof where the equipment and generator are located.

We are now lying next to the running generator. I inform 102 that we have reached our destination. We switch the generator's power off, fill the tank, check the spark plugs and oil, and finally restart it. The good thing is that we are able to perform the entire task while still lying and hiding.

All goes as planned. The maintenance operation takes a little over 20 minutes. The good news is that it is almost entirely dark now and snipers cannot aim at us anymore. Night vision instruments were not yet widely available. The bad news is that we have to climb down the building in sheer darkness. Flashlights are definitely not an option.

I close the jerrican while Eiffel radioes 102 informing them of our readiness to head back to base. It is easier than we anticipated. Each time we reach the side of the stairs that are invisible to snipers; I fire up my Zippo for a fraction of a second to check our way.

We finally make it to the ground floor, where Boss, Kebbeh, and Shorty are anxiously waiting. We crack a couple jokes while heading back to 102 for dinner. Tonight was Kebbeh's turn to bring in the food.

(Eby)
A PINT FOR A LIFE
1984

Many are the horrors of war. Abundant stories stand as perennial testimonies, monuments of shame. When everyone dies and everything perishes only those monuments remain, a legacy left by a race whose arrogance and ignorance made it oblivious to how insignificant it is and the extent of damage it inflicted.

Of all those horrors and stories, only one subject obliterates all others... children. They are the silent victims, the carriers of innocence. The more children die in wars, the less innocence is left on Earth; no wonder why there is more evil and more wars.

The earliest memory I have of children killed, injured, or displaced by war is from the Vietnam conflict. When we used to live in the old Gemmayzeh building, we did not have a TV set. My maternal Aunt Isabelle lived one floor beneath us. Isabelle is a wonderful woman and I love her as much as I love Mom. Her husband Jamil, a peaceful, understated, and often silent man had a heart of gold. He co-owned a home appliance store in downtown Beirut. He passed away in the late 70s from a stroke after he lost his store and everything he owned in downtown Beirut, which became the main civil war front line. Isabelle and Jamil had a black and white TV set. Every evening, after finishing our studies, Jad and I were allowed to go down to Tante Iso's and watch the 6:30 p.m. cartoon show. I remember watching a glimpse of the early news rundown before the start of my favorite cartoon show, Heckle and Jeckle. I vividly recall the black and white overexposed footage showing naked children running scared, mothers holding blood-covered toddlers fleeing, and mutilated bodies of babies lying in the mud.

The civil war in Lebanon, just as in Vietnam or any other conflict, does not spare the children. In a country where the age average is low, the young ones are often the first to go. Even the majority of fighters and militiamen are young, some as young as 15 years old. Ask Jad. They carry guns and kill enemies as young as them. One might argue that they chose this path; they might have indeed, but the question remains: Who allowed, encouraged, indoctrinated, and recruited them? And what would the alternate path have been?

Then, there are the innocent ones, those who are at school or home, walking in the street or hiding in a shelter, playing in their backyard, or crouching in a corner of their bedroom traumatized, scared to death by the horrifying whistle of an incoming mortar. There are so many of them. Some died, some are crippled for life. While others made it, they were still not spared by war. The trauma, the psychological scars, are the one memory they crave to erase. Jad and I belong to this generation, eternally haunted by the specters of those years past. While those who died are the one-time martyrs, survivors are the everyday ones.

102 is one of the few Red Cross Centers in Lebanon that houses a blood bank. Blood banks exist in one of the Centers of every region of the country. Blood donations are scarce, and most of the banks' supplies come from abroad. Many issues plague the availability; types of blood, mostly the rare ones, are always the first to run dry. Expiry date of

the supplies is another problem, and reluctantly, pints of blood have to be thrown away. Electricity is another worry. Although all blood banks have emergency generators, even fuel goes missing during heavy bombardment, and the fridges holding the precious commodity come to a halt, sending the entire stock to waste.

Numerous are the times where Red Cross volunteers had to offer their own blood in emergencies, when no alternative could be found.

It is a sunny day in Beirut and, like on most sunny days in the civil war, fighting rages. The cold and rain are a handicap to fighters, so much that Lebanese people keep wishing for endless winters.

The streets are empty and a sudden lull casts an eerie silence, only broken by the occasional chirp of a brave bird. Lulls last for half an hour, enough for the warring parties to replenish their ammunition stocks, and then hell breaks loose again.

102's blood bank receives a request for two pints of A+ blood type, the second most common type. Paradoxically, and because it is one of the most common, it sometimes is the hardest to find. Today, 102 is out of A+.

I am manning the radio shift with Kebbeh next to me.

– *102, 102. 101.*

– *101. 102.*

It is customary in radio communication to always state the party you are calling twice, followed once by the calling party.

– *102, HDF* (Hôtel-Dieu de France hospital) *needs 2*

units of A+. Urgent.

– *Let me check,* answers Kebbeh. He puts down the microphone. *Eby, please stay on the radio while I check the blood bank.*

Kebbeh disappears for few seconds and comes back.

– *Eby, tell 101 we're out of A+.*

– *101, 101. 102.*

– *102. 101.*

– *Sorry guys, but we're out of A+.*

– *Stand by 102.*

Fifteen seconds of radio silence, and then:

– *102. 101.*

– *Yes, 101.*

– *102, this is an emergency. A 4-year-old girl wounded and losing blood profusely.*

I take my thumb off the radio "talk" button and look at Kebbeh for a second.

– *Kebbeh, I'm A+. Drive me to HDF now.*

– *Are you sure?*

– *Positive.*

– *Fine. Let's go. Inform 101.*

I press the radio button for two seconds without saying a word, then:

– *101. 102.*

– *Yes, 102.*

– *This is Spirou. I'm A+. I can give one pint. Leaving for HDF now.*

– *Great, Spirou. Thanks. We'll inform HDF. Go directly to ER and ask for the blood bank.*

– *Positive. Thank you.*

Kebbeh is ready with the keys of the 176 Volvo ambulance. He is wearing his helmet and carrying one for me. We immediately leave for HDF after informing the rest of the team.

Why did I not tell Kebbeh or 101 that I am anemic? I am underweight for my age and giving blood is not a good idea. We reach the hospital and promptly head for the blood bank. There, only one male nurse is waiting for us. There is no need for more, the HDF blood bank fridges are empty. They have been out of stock for months now.

The nurse preps me and inserts the needle as I look away. Damn! How I hate needles! The warm red elixir of life starts flowing. One pint exactly. The nurse pulls the needle out and places an alcohol-soaked cotton ball on the needle-mark and asks me to bend my arm and hold the swab in place. He also gives me a small orange juice pack to drink.

Kebbeh notices that I am turning pale and sweat beads appear my forehead.

– *Hey buddy! Are you ok?*

– *Um, yeah, yeah, I'm fine. A bit dizzy but fine.*

I am not fine at all. A pint of blood for someone who needed every drop of it is a pint too much. I could barely lift my head, let alone stand up at all; my lips and tongue are dry and numb. Kebbeh sticks the straw in the juice carton.

– Here, drink this. It'll make you feel better.

We wait until I felt better and make it back to 102. But before we leave HDF, I insist on asking the nurse about the victim and whether I could call back and inquire about her.

– It's a girl, says the nurse. *She is 4 years old and has been hit by shrapnel straight in her artery. Luckily, her parents managed to get her to ER on time. We still don't know if she will make it through. She needs the blood.*

– Can I call you back for news on her situation?

– Sure, call the blood bank at HDF and ask for me, Imad.

It takes me the entire morning to feel better. I remain lying in bed at 102, and the guys bring me more juice and sugar-rich food. Early in the afternoon, I pick up the phone and call HDF.

– Can I speak to Imad in the blood bank please?

After minutes of waiting:

– This is Imad.

– Hey, it's Ibrahim from the Red Cross. I was there this morning to give blood for the wounded little girl.

– Oh yes, I remember you.

– Is she fine?

– Well, you're not going to believe it, but it is your pint of blood that saved her life.

– Are you serious?

– Yes. She badly needed blood. They were about to lose her. They had almost depleted all the A+ stock they had, until I got to the operation theatre with your pint. We told her

parents the story, and how we managed to get that pint. They want to meet you and thank you.

– No, no. Tell them I can't. Tell them I'm on a mission and thank them. You know what? Tell them I was simply doing my job.

I have a lot to think about now. I could not believe it. I just saved the life of a little girl.

One pint for one life. How many more pints is it going to take?

(Eby)
TWO INCHES IS ALL YOU NEED
WHEN LIFE IS AT STAKE
1984

I have been in love since Christmas of 1978. It is now 1982, and Aline and I have been together for almost 4 years.

Aline studied Interior Design but decided later to shift to Graphic Design. She joined one of the leading advertising agencies in Beirut. The agency is located on "Mathaf", the National Museum road, one of the hottest fronts on the Green Line that separates East Beirut from its West. The National Museum is now located in the heart of the no-man's land. The building housing Aline's agency is the last before the no-man's land. Ten-foot-high dirt mounds and empty shipping containers cut the road and protect the civilians from snipers. Beyond the artificial hill, on bad days, fierce battles take place and no one comes to work.

As strange as it may sound, most Lebanese still go to work in neighborhoods bordering the front line. My barber shop is located on the Beirut downtown front even farther from 102 and, by all standards, is considered a hazardous area.

Driving to "Mathaf" and back is not an easy ride. One must know which streets to take and the ones to avoid. One must also learn to listen to the ominous signs of a battle in the making. Aline and I, just like most Lebanese living on the frontlines, have learned to read those signs.

Before the civil war, the National Museum area and the adjacent Badaro street were one of the hippest, where politicians and the wealthy lived in lush vintage apartments. There also, to the right of the Museum on the large intersection, is the monument to the Unknown Soldier, beautifully nested under large granite Roman pillars similar to the ones found in the majestic Baalbeck. Now, militias use these buildings as bunkers and headquarters. Most of the apartments have been ransacked and the contents can be purchased in a flourishing black market.

I left the agency I worked for in Badaro about a year ago. It was located a few blocks away from Aline's work. Now I work for another advertising agency located on the Sin El Fil highway, 20 minutes away from Aline's by car. Every evening, I leave work and drive to "Mathaf" to pick her up and drive home. She also lives in Gemmayzeh, but on the upper street parallel to where I live.

On good days, I park my 1973 "Renault 5" in front of the building's main entrance next to the dirt hill and wait for Aline to come down. Her office overlooks the street, so I honk to let her know I'm here. On days when fighting rages, I drive through the Badaro Street side, which is perpendicular to "Mathaf" then make a right and park behind Aline's building where it is relatively safer. She would then walk a narrow alley between her office building and the one next to it, that leads to where I wait.

It is a cool March afternoon. The fragrance of jasmine trees lining the gardens of the lush Badaro buildings fills the air. Fighting is bad today and skirmishes have erupted around noon on the Green Line. I thought it would be safer to pick up Aline from the office's backside today.

While waiting, I remember the day I had to come in an ambulance to drive her home. Her boss is one of those ruthless owners that care only for the business, never the staff. As long as he thinks he can stay, everyone else has to comply. That day, he went a bit too far. Fighting had erupted right next to Aline's office and spread all over Beirut. On the news, anchors warn people to stay home or in shelters.

I had to drive to "Mathaf" in an ambulance with Boss under the heavy shelling. I still vividly remember how that day I stood on the street below Aline's office, switched the ambulance' siren on, and shouted from the bottom of my lungs, insulting her boss and asking her to immediately come down. All the agency's staff rushed to the balcony to get a glimpse of Aline's Romeo coming to the rescue. That night, most of the remaining staff that did not heed the warning got stuck in the office for 2 days without food or electricity.

I am still waiting for Aline. I can't honk; she is too far to hear when I arrive from the back. I usually call her before I leave work and tell her to come down in exactly 20 minutes. I know I will make it earlier. I prefer not to let her wait alone on the street.

I step out of the car, light a cigarette, and lean against the fenced wall of a garden on the corner of the main road and a street that leads back to Badaro. It's a low old ochre sandstone wall, fenced with 4-foot-high iron bars elaborately cast in beautiful floral shapes. I am thinking of our engagement. We have set the date as April 6, a Friday. I am thrilled and anxious at the same time. I realize more and more how much of a big move this is. I am having doubts about my abilities to build a family. After I witnessed what happened to us: my father's death, the war, I can't stop thinking about how I will sail that ocean on my own.

From where I stand, I can peek straight ahead into the street and see a part of the National Museum clad with sand bags to protect it. Beyond the Museum is the rest of the no-man's land.

As I carefully tilt my head two inches to the right to try and get a better view, I hear a quick whistle, feel a burn in my scalp, right above my right ear and, simultaneously, the impact of metal objects colliding.

Instinctively, I duck putting my hand over my head and look at my palm. It had a small streak of blood on it. I am hit. Damn! I think how can it be? Snipers are not supposed to reach this street! Maybe I misjudged that narrow opening overlooking the Museum. Ideas and nightmares rush through my head. I know from my Red Cross training that some sniper bullets, mainly from M16 rifles, do not hurt immediately after they hit the target. I wait to start feeling the pain, thinking the bullet is lodged inside my head. I do not dare to touch the wound again, fearing the worst.

I definitely do not want to die now. So, that's what it feels to be hit by a sniper bullet. I look toward the alley from which Aline is supposed to come; I don't want her to panic. I finally gather enough courage to reach once more for my head and slowly feel the wound. Nothing has changed. There's still not too much blood; there's even less. As I look at my hand while still crouching, I notice on the ground the remains of a bullet. I reach and grab it. It was still slightly warm, an indication that this might be the one that hit me. So, I am not going to die after all. I look back at the fence and see the impact point. The bullet has hit and warped one of the iron-cast poles and fell on the ground.

I smile, then I frown, then I smile again. Now, I realize how incredibly lucky I was. At the exact moment when I tilted my head, the bullet hit. It took just 2 inches to save my life. I pick up the bullet pieces, wrap them in a tissue paper, sit in the car, lean back, and finish what could have been my last cigarette. My scalp is slightly burning, but everything is going to be fine. As I take the last sip, Aline shows up and waves. I raise my hand in a stop sign. She freezes. I start the car and cross the street. I prefer to pick her up there. I do not want to take any more risks. From now on, when I meet her from the back I will always park on the right, and safely stay in the car.

I recount my ordeal to Aline but only when we reach Gemmayzeh. She cries and begs me not to pick her up anymore. I smile and tell her that now I understand why everyone says love kills.

(Eby)
THE ENGAGEMENT
1984

Speaking of cheating death, I had made a promise to Aline on January 5, 1980. I took an oath to marry her on January 5, 1985. We were both crazy. There was not a single chance it could happen from where we stood back then. She was still studying, and I had been working officially for only 2 years and my monthly income was around $300 in today's dollars, before taxes.

Aline and I decide to get engaged on April 6, 1984. That is one date no one in Lebanon would ever forget. It is remembered still as one of the most intense fighting nights in the Lebanese Civil War annals. Most of the engagement ceremony happened in the bathroom of Aline's house, considered as the safest room in the house – not that it actually was.

Over time, the Lebanese grew a false sense of both security and reality. If a room is small, it must be safe. If it has two or more walls within the house, it is considered a good shelter. We are trying to convince ourselves that we are safe. So many innocent people died while enjoying that sensation. Bombs and snipers do not discriminate. They do not rely on your emotion, nor does the latter shield you from their evil. In our house, Jad and I considered our bedroom to be the safest room in the house. We used to hide there during heavy shelling, huddling against each other on the floor, and leaning against the cupboards.

That bedroom, where Jad and I sleep and where we used to hide with Mom, was hit by a mortar that tore its façade off as well as the balcony of the floor above. Luckily, it was summer, and we were in Jouret El Termos (where we used to spend the summer).

There is no safe room during war. There are only false sensations of safety.

Aline and her parents live on the third floor of an old typical Lebanese post-World War II building on the upper street of Gemmayzeh. The place is cozy and well furnished; it has been my second home for 4 years now. I spent countless hours in the living and dining rooms, playing guitar with Aline, or helping her with her university projects.

Mom, Jad, and I arrive to Aline's home for the traditional ritual. In Lebanon, the bride organizes the engagement ceremony. The husband-to-be comes to her home to symbolize him asking her parents' permission to wed her. They had prepared an amazing dinner, a very rich menu. Also present were Aline's sister and her husband. Everything is simply perfect. Aline is looking beautiful in a light dress and simple makeup. The evening starts on a wonderful note, chatting, laughing. I present Aline with the engagement ring. We cut the traditional engagement cake and get seated for dinner.

While being served the salad, we start hearing far but frequent explosions, typical of a battle starting on the front. Aline's house is located slightly closer to the front then ours.

At first, we are simply concerned. After all, it has been 9 years since the civil war started. We became experts at guessing the signs of a battle, its whereabouts, and intensity. Fifteen minutes later, the shellings' frequency increases, the explosions intensify, and become noticeably close. Doors and windows rattle with every blast, and we could guess that the mortar shells are starting to fall close by in the neighborhood.

Now is a good time to panic. In a reflex, everyone runs toward the small bathroom. All except Aline, Jad, and me.

It's an awkward and funny situation, almost surreal. Jad and I are so used to similar situations. In fact, we are supposed to be on the front in such times. We are embarrassed... hungry and embarrassed. So, while Mom tries to squeeze herself in the bathroom with the rest of the family, Jad, my fiancée, and I are having dinner and trying to guess where the shells are originating, their caliber, and where they are landing. We are nevertheless feeling a bit edgy; I should be at 102 now.

Aline's mother keeps shouting calling us to join them and hide. Aline and I crack jokes about how we could squeeze 7 people in the tiny bathroom that could barely hold one.

Somewhere deep inside of me, I ponder over my luck, and then I am not laughing at all. I would love to remember my engagement party forever, but not like that.

The strange night ends finally. We all wait until the shelling winds down, and we rush home as swiftly as possible.

(Eby)
WEDDINGS AND TEARS
1985

Saturday, January 5, 1985.

My promise is kept. I am 25 years old and Aline is 24. Today we are getting married at the same church where my father's funeral service was held 13 years ago. The weather is better now after an early light shower and there's no fighting or shelling. All is great except for one thing: tomorrow, Jad is leaving the country for good to go work in the Gulf countries.

The Gulf, mostly Saudi Arabia and the United Arab Emirates, became a prime destination for the Lebanese fleeing the civil war to make a living. The pay is high and accommodation is provided. In many cases, the perks include a car and even food.

Jad is going to Fujairah, United Arab Emirates (UAE). The tiny emirate is the only one located on the Indian Ocean, hence its active Port.

Jad is now officially engaged to Josette, one of my teammates at 102; the one I kissed on Valentine's Day at Delta. Jijo's (Josette's nickname) father works for a large livestock import business with offices located on the premises of the Fujairah Port. Jad will work for him and will soon wed his daughter.

By 1986, Jad and I had both resigned from the Red Cross. Unfortunately, there is no reservist policy. We would have loved to remain as reservists and be called upon in time of crisis or shortage. After all, the accumulated experience and what we both went through constitute a gold mine of knowledge. I broke all the rules and refused to hand over my badge, overall, and bib. These are the only real souvenirs I will take with me for life, show to my children one day while telling them my and their uncle's story. I still have them to this day.

It is not easy for Mom and me seeing Jad leave for good. Since our father's demise, we were never separated. Neither Jad nor I know how we will feel about it. So, my happiness is not whole on this day. Just like on my engagement day, luck keeps chasing me.

With the financial help of our uncles, and my Mom and aunts' creativity, I manage to organize quite an impressive wedding followed by a small cocktail hour at home for relatives and closest friends. The church is packed. Aline and I, both Graphic Designers, have designed our own special wedding card and went on a tour of the country to distribute the invitations.

Most of 102 attends the wedding ceremony and manages to crack a few jokes during the service. At the end, when the priest says, "*You may kiss the bride,*" a roar surges in the church asking for a mouth-to-mouth kiss. Even Jad, the best man is part of the plan. As a newlywed couple, we indulge. One of the cousins has small firecrackers hidden on him and ignites them in the church. The priest is furious, which made everyone else laugh even more.

The bride is gorgeous in her retro wedding dress. I am dressed in a dark grey suit and white bowtie. We drive back home for the cocktail hour with the family, a 3-minute ride.

We had ordered a small but beautiful white wedding cake. Mom brought out the silver cutlery and rock crystal champagne flutes. Everything she had from her own wedding is now on the dining table. The close family, friends, and Team 1 from 102 are there. It is champagne time; I clumsily manage to break the cork inside the bottle instead of popping it. For some, this is a sign of my "physical" performance, and now it is all documented on tape.

During the entire party, Jad and I exchange looks. We both know it will be a hard separation. For years now, our relationship has been growing stronger and an invisible but unbreakable bond is established.

Finally, Aline and I leave for our weekend honeymoon at the San Antonio hotel in the Faraya snowy mountains. Jad finishes packing and gets ready to head to the UAE the very next morning.

This is one too many separations for our mother to handle. In the flip of a day she finds herself alone, in an empty home, with no husband or children. She was only 49 years old!

(Jad)
THE FUJAIRAH ROLLER COASTER
1985

When things happen for a reason, the reason is seldom announced until your course of life takes a dramatic turn.

As I was getting tired of working for my uncle, I had enough with the moral abuse and enough of living in the limbo of an obscure future; I was gifted with an opportunity for change. A chemical and mechanical engineering company in Ashrafieh, not far from home, was looking for someone in Sales. Tony, my cousin and 102 teammate, worked there. As soon as he heard about the opening, he called asking if I was interested and I was indeed. I came in for an interview and got the job. I was a good Salesman, and good Salesmen know how to sell themselves first. It was a good and rewarding job. Unfortunately, good things were never meant to last. Although I knew that quite well I always dreaded when they came to an abrupt halt, and that time the brute G-force of the sudden disappointment was overwhelming. The owner of the company, a very decent guy, was assassinated for some reason, still unknown till today. Consequently, the company had to close.

I was dating Josette then, also a 102 first-responder and a teammate of Eby. Now that's one interesting story! The line between deception and cunning is very thin, and as the saying goes, "it is the end that justifies the means."

Just so you know, at first Josette was not interested in

me at all. I remember asking her a number of times to go out, but she always turned me down. I'm tenacious, and my resolve has proven time and again to be an asset, and indeed it was. Josette finally agreed to go to the movies with me. From there on things started steadily evolving toward a serious relationship. But at 102, I was swimming in a pool of sharks. Two of my fellow first-responders, who were by far more well off than I was, were swarming all over her and asking her out several times.

I have to admit that Josette was a heart-throb. Attractive and regularly suntanned, she always came to 102 in her skimpy jean shorts and blond hair, turning heads in her wake. Her father lived and worked in the United Arab Emirates, a tan-seekers haven. She used to travel there often with her siblings to spend vacations or flee the civil war, hence her rare but precious appearances at 102.

Josette drove a large brown Chevrolet, and finding a parking space in the narrow street of 102 was virtually impossible, let alone for an oversized vehicle like hers. I remember most of the adrenaline-charged males rushing to the rescue and offering to park it for her.

That's where my cunning came in handy... or deception; depending on how one looks at it.

My tactic was simple. I approached each of the contenders individually and told each that Josette and I have been going out for a while now and that we are romantically involved, very involved... and it worked. They backed off. The funny part was that Josette, puzzled, was wondering why they both suddenly and simultaneously abandoned their courtship. I knew that she was trying to keep her options open and did have some interest in both.

Now the ground was all mine, and I went all the way.

After going out for a few months, Josette introduced me to her parents. Joseph, her father, was a retired high-ranking officer in the *"Sûreté Générale"*, the Lebanese equivalent of both the FBI and NSA. He spent most of his time in Fujairah, the most remote emirate in the United Arab Emirates federation. There, he managed a company located in the Port Free Zone and traded in livestock transshipment between Australia, his main supplier, and the Gulf and Arab countries.

When he heard about my lost job, my father-in-law-to-be offered me to travel to Fujairah and join his company. This meant leaving Lebanon for good, becoming an expatriate. Although Joseph and I did not see eye to eye and had fundamental differences, I said to myself what the heck! I accepted.

Another nightmare had just begun. It started the moment I landed in the UAE.

I still vividly remember boarding the airplane in Lebanon, from the same airport where Dad used to take Eby and me to watch the planes take off and land. I had butterflies in my stomach, it was the first time in my life that I boarded an airplane, let alone fly in one. I was at the same time happy and scared, but could not show it to Joseph so he does not make fun of me.

It was January 6, 1985. Eby got married yesterday afternoon.

Upon landing at Dubai Airport, we were picked up by Ahmed, Joseph's driver. A sandstorm was raging that night; it was the first time I witnessed one for real. We were driving almost completely blind as visibility on the highway was reduced to a few feet. Everything was red, including the inside of the car despite the closed windows.

The drive to Fujairah took 5 hours. Ahmed was not only Joseph's driver, but also his eyes and ears while he was away. During our drive, he was filling him in on all the happenings while he was away.

Upon our arrival, Joseph showed me the compound where he lived, and which consisted of the main quarters and a guest house, the whole property surrounded by a 6-foot wall. He gave me a tour of the premises then pointed to the guest house, telling me that this was where I will be staying. I thought I would get to live in the main quarters with him, which were big enough to accommodate both of us. Don't be fooled by the words "guest house", it was more of a double room in a cheap motel. These houses were meant for local Arabs who lived strictly by the Muslim law (Sharia) that dictated a separation between genders, hence the main quarters and guest house. The complex was usually built around a central garden and covered parking spaces. Central air conditioning was slowly making its way into homes, but for now, most buildings still had noisy window units.

I chose one of the two available rooms, unpacked and went to take a well-deserved shower, only to find a huge cockroach roaming freely in a bathtub that looked unused for years. I hate roaches, and that dates back to when I was 12 or 13. Ironically, I also was having a shower at home, and as I came out of the tub and put on my bathrobe, a cockroach the size of a bat was hiding inside and fell right on... my private parts. Since then, I developed an uncontrollable phobia for roaches.

The irony of life. I left one Uncle Joseph's clothing shop having had enough being treated with disdain, only to go work for yet another "Uncle" Joseph, where the same treatment is amplified, miles away from home. How is that one might ask? Read on.

While settling inside the primitive guest house, Khan, the Pakistani housekeeper cum cook, stepped in and asked me to join Joseph for dinner. Actually, I was more told than asked. He informed me that there was grilled fish on the menu. I hated fish. Once in the master's quarters, I tried explaining to Joseph my distaste for fish, but he authoritatively replied that I had to start getting used to it, because we lived on the shore of the Indian Ocean where fish was abundant and healthy. I had fish for dinner that night, and it was horrible. It brought back memories of Mom and me arguing about my finicky food taste. Once finished, I was dismissed and told by Joseph to meet him the next morning at 8:00 a.m. sharp for breakfast.

That was the most substantial breakfast I ever had. Omelets, cheese, olives, and dates. Joseph loved dates; a staple food of the Gulf countries, he ate them with practically everything. We finished breakfast and drove to work. There, Joseph introduced me to "Mr." Kumar (that is how he wanted me to call him), the Pakistani General Manager. Kumar was 6 feet 4 inches tall, 240 pounds, and with a dark skin pigmented by large white patches, a severe case of vitiligo. I could immediately sense the animosity; it was as if he felt threatened. He probably thought I was there to take his place. I was later told that few years back, one of Joseph's nephews came to work and also made Kumar feel threatened and uncomfortable. For me, that was not a healthy first day at work. Kumar walked me out to the parking area and pointed at an old and smelly Mazda.

"This will be your company car." he said. The wreck belonged to the veterinarian and had no climate control.

I gave it my best; I was friendly, almost submissive. I nicely asked Kumar to teach me the ropes, but he was disinclined provide me with the right training, which made my assimilation painfully slow. I was mad, and from that day on, my relationship with Kumar went downhill, and got even worse with Joseph.

During my early days in Fujairah, Joseph and I used to play tennis at the Hilton hotel and beach resort. We then drove to the fish market for the fresh catch and back home to get it cooked and have long dinners drowned in an ocean of scotch whiskey. I hated that routine; Fujairah was boring. There was nothing else to do, no movie theaters, no shopping malls, no parks, absolutely nothing had we not had the Hilton.

Being the most remote emirate in the Federation, Fujairah was isolated, rarely visited by locals or tourists. Facing the Indian Ocean, it was embedded in a valley, surrounded by black iron ore and volcanic rock mountains. It took about an hour to reach from Sharjah, on a highway stretching through the desert. On the way, few settlements and date plantations punctuated the deep red sand hills; which, as you drove nearer to Fujairah, blended with the mountains' eroded soil and morphed into a darker shade of brown.

Even the tennis and fish market routine started decaying and degrading slowly as a result of the friction with Joseph, both at work and home. Luckily, he used to travel often on business trips, which provided me with breathing space.

I was at work one day when he returned from a lengthy trip. He came storming into the office and straight to my desk, yelling in front of everyone:

– Who the hell gave you the permission to come to work at 10 a.m, step inside the office while whistling, and have the nerve to park your car in my spot under the shed?

I was flabbergasted, speechless at first. It took me few seconds to gather enough strength to reply:

– First, I was here on time, 9:00 a.m. sharp, and yes, I was whistling, but outside while walking from my car to the office. As for the parking, where's the problem? The space was empty, and hey! It is burning hot outside, why can't I use the covered car park?

Joseph went ballistic, yelling at me even louder telling me that I am not the boss here, even when he's traveling. I honestly never thought of myself as the boss. I had to keep my mouth shut, which drained most of my patience and ego.

Like the accommodation and company car, food was part of my remuneration package. This was a widely spread trend in the Gulf countries in early years. Back then, the need for manpower was overwhelming but the living standards and forbidding weather conditions ruled the area out of consideration for of most of the available skilled workforce, mostly from other Arab countries like Lebanon, Syria, and Jordan. What lured them was the package. Free furnished accommodation, company car, food, one-month vacation, and the yearly round trip ticket home.

I used to buy what I needed to feed myself and present the bills to Kumar to get reimbursed at the end of the month. I never imagined he would go through the bills trying to build a case against me.

One afternoon, Joseph called me to his office to tell me how disappointed he was because I was irresponsible and taking advantage of him. As I inquired why, he replied that one of my bills showed that I had purchased smoked salmon which, according to him, was a waste of money. I was outraged. I told him that I did not buy any salmon and reminded him that I hated fish. He looked at me perplexed, then stood up and rushed to Kumar's desk asking him where he got the proof that I had purchased smoked salmon. Embarrassed, Kumar started yelling incomprehensibly to cover up his lie, pretending to look among my supply bills for the incriminating invoice. I walked in and got into a loud argument with him. I was so furious and out of control that I held the desk and flipped it on him, and then tried reaching over it to land a punch on his face. He threatened to call the police while colleagues were trying to hold me back and calm me down. I rushed out of the office and drove home. That night, Joseph and I did not see each other. The next morning, he left town and I called a friend, Tony, who also lived in Fujairah and was very well connected. After telling him about my ordeal, he strongly recommended that I should tone things down before getting myself into some serious trouble.

Without telling me, Tony later called Joseph, whom he knew well before I did, and complained to him about the way he was treating me. Joseph never listened to anyone, and once back, he came straight to me infuriated about the fact that I had told Tony. That day we had our biggest argument so far. I tried once more to reason with him, telling him that I did not buy the salmon, and that having been a big shot officer in the Intelligence field he should know better and carry out a full investigation rather than unjustifiably accusing and judging people. This vexed him even more. He cut the discussion short asking me to eat my dinner and go to sleep. I was not hungry. I immediately left.

Manure, a by-product of the livestock business, was collected on site, packaged and sold as fertilizer. Workers, mostly Asians, earned 3 Dirhams (roughly 85 cents) for every bag filled. Planning on making some extra cash, I decided to fill manure bags on my spare time. When Joseph found out, through Kumar of course, he spilled his wrath on me, one more time solemnly stating that no one can do anything in the company without his permission.

Joseph was the father of Josette and my father-in-law-to-be, and that complicated things further. I missed Josette and used to send her cassette recordings and letters telling her about my days every time Joseph flew to Beirut. Phone calls were not that easy to make and cost a lot of money. Besides, I did not want to get into more arguments with Joseph about over spending. We were planning to wed a few months from now, in June. I later found out that Jijo, that was her nickname, also used to send me recordings and letters with her father to check on me, and that most of which were never delivered. The more I thought about it, the more I realized that most of Joseph's resentment was not directed toward me as Jad, but rather toward me as his future son-in-law. Why would he want to marry his daughter to someone like me? I was financially deprived, fatherless, and with minimum education. For once, I agreed that I would not be any father's first choice, let alone someone as protective as Joseph. I could not argue with that. My self-confidence was taking a deep dive, and my future felt smothered by a thick fog of uncertainty.

I was often compelled to mingle and socialize with Joseph's friends, old boring people with whom I had nothing in common. I craved meeting and going out with people my own age but Joseph forced me to stay with him and his bunch, spending endless nights watching bottles of whiskey getting drained to the last drop. Tony, our common friend, used to often call asking Joseph to let me go out with him and his friends, but Joseph refused.

It was now June 1985, 6 months since I had left Beirut. When I think of all that has happened in just half a year, I couldn't help but dread the months and years to come. I finally flew back to Beirut to get married to Josette. It is needless to say that the entire wedding was planned, orchestrated, and executed by Joseph. As for me, the only souvenir I still carry is how disastrous it was. I almost had a fight with Joseph during the cocktail party. Josette and I flew back to Fujairah a few days later, and into the same old guest house.

Work was getting harder. I was often sent to other ports around Fujairah to oversee the unloading of livestock shipments, which would mostly start at sundown and stretch throughout the entire night, to avoid the grueling daylight temperatures. I would return home around 5:00 a.m., exhausted and reeking. The stench of manure on my clothes and skin was so unbearable, that I had to undress outside and shower in the car park with a garden hose before I could step into the guest house. I did not have enough time to sit with my wife. After we got married, we did not even have a honeymoon. Josette became depressed, spending long hours sitting on the front porch, crying, and wondering how we ended up here.

A year had passed when I decided to bring my Mother to Fujairah. Her presence next to Josette will help. They were extremely close ever since they first met. In fact, Josette almost moved in with my Mom while I was alone in Fujairah. I thought of issuing her with a 3-year renewable residence visa, allowing her to come and go as she pleased. Nadia came to Fujairah a few times; once with Eby after I arranged a job interview for him in Dubai which ultimately earned him a position in an advertising agency in January 1986.

As months passed, my relationship with Tony got stronger. Now that I was married and lived – almost – alone with my wife, her father's grip on me loosened enough to allow me more freedom to meet the people I wanted. Noticing my suffering, Tony set on a mission to help me land a job with the insurance company he ran. Al-Fujairah National Insurance Company had an opening at their Dubai office. This was the breakthrough I was hoping and praying for. We packed and moved to Sharjah emirate, which was 20 minutes away from my office in Dubai. Obviously, Joseph was furious with me, his daughter, and Tony. But there was nothing he could do. Not anymore.

My new job was great and rewarding and opened up the exclusive scene of Dubai and Europe to me. From there, destiny finally helped me realize my dream of living in the United States of America. And here I am.

Remember the endless hours sitting on the balcony watching the planes coming to land? Remember the trips to the airport with my Dad? Remember the disappointment of knowing that I will never be a pilot? When I moved to Miami I started taking flying lessons, and now I earned my Private Pilot license and my dream came true. This taught me a valuable lesson, that time is not the enemy of dreams. Time is a dream's best partner.

From that afternoon of January 6th, 1985, when I flew to Fujairah a few hours after Eby's wedding, to this day, I never regretted any decision I made. I do not regret any of the bad things that happened to me. Each decision and happening had a spectacular impact on the course of my life; each played a small part in the big scheme that brought me to be a citizen in the land of the free.

On June 29, 1985 I returned from Fujairah to get married in Beirut, exactly 6 months after Eby's wedding. The reunion is a very happy moment for everyone. Aline and Eby also designed our wedding cards.

Josette looked gorgeous. This time it is Eby's turn to be the best man, and he insisted on playing the "mouth-to-mouth" prank on me, but I was quicker and did not need an invitation.

Almost the entire crew of 102 attended my wedding at the same church where Eby was wed 6 months earlier. Same cousins with firecrackers were there, as was the same ranting priest – who this time swore never to marry anyone from the Lahoud family ever again. He did not have to swear; he had just married the last one.

I loved to have things my own way, especially when the decision belongs to me in the first place. On the other hand, my father-in-law is a retired military man used to giving orders and having them executed without rebuttal. He does not care much whose decision it should be. As far as he is concerned, your opinion belongs to him. You do the math.

Josette and I were in agreement over the type of

wedding we wanted to have, but my future father-in-law had a different plan. After all, and in his mind, it was the wedding of his eldest daughter and the first in the family. We kept clashing over it until after the wedding and even during the large dinner party that the ex-colonel had planned and held even though Josette and I were very much against it.

Ultimately, the night ended and we flew back to Fujairah. Not long after Eby and I had a long discussion about bringing him over to the United Arab Emirates so we could be reunited again.

(Eby)
THE MIRACLE OF WINNING YOUR LIFE BACK
1985

It is already October. Jad has been in the United Arab Emirates for 4 months. Through his connections in Fujairah and Dubai, he manages to secure a job interview for me with an advertising agency based in Dubai. I will have to fly there via Damascus, Syria. Access to the Beirut airport is quite hazardous and virtually impossible from East Beirut, especially for Christians. Ironically, traveling through Syria is a safer route. I would later wish I took the risk of driving to the airport over the one of going through Damascus.

Taxis to Damascus leave Bourj Hammoud in Beirut at 2:00 a.m. and arrive on time to catch the morning plane to Dubai. I chose to spend the night at Mom's and then take a cab to the taxi station at 1:30 a.m.

We board an old Buick with four other passengers and the driver. The ride is smooth. We cross a couple of militias' barrages without any problems and reach the International border. We cross Masnaa, the Lebanese side checkpoint of the border with Syria, and reach the Jdeideh customs checkpoint on the Syrian side. Taxi drivers have clear instructions by the Syrian military to leave the passengers inside the vehicle and come inside the checkpoint office alone with their passports. It is 4:00 a.m. and still dark.

A few minutes later, the taxi driver returned and everyone sighs with relief. Finally, the trip can resume. But

الجمهورية العربية السورية
ادارة المخابرات العامة
الفرع ٢٥١

الى من يهمه الامر

راجعنا المدعو أحمد تيم لمور .... والدته نادرة
تولد عام ١٩٥٩ من أهالي .... بيت لره
التابعة لمحافظة جبل لبنان ....
يسمح له بحرية التنقل والمغادرة لكونه خلاف المقصود
بال .... سم ج ....
رقم / .... / ١٩٤٢ / ب / .... تاريخ ٨٨/٨/١٩٨٢
ويسحب هذا الاشعار في آخر مركز للهجرة .

دمشق ٨٨/٣٠٠/ ١٩٨٠   مدير ادارة المخابرات العامة
بالتفويض
رئيس الفرع ٢٥١

I still keep the yellow piece of paper handed to me by the syrian secret service
"branch 251" and which allowed me to leave the country.

the driver comes from the passenger side and asks:

– *Who is Ibrahim Lahoud?*

– *Me,* I answer, puzzled.

– *Come down. They want to talk to you.*

I can feel and even hear my heart beat. I look around me as if trying to get an answer from the other passengers who are already getting upset. Now they have to wait even more. I step out of the car and walk behind the driver toward the customs office like a man on death row. I never felt so scared in my life. I have such a bad feeling about this. Once we reach the main door, the driver lets me in, pointing to the counter at the end of the large hall, turns back and starts walking to his car.

– *Hey! Wait! Wait! Where are you going?* I Shout.

– *I have other passengers. I can't wait. I'll unload your luggage and leave it there, by the door.*

For a second, the darkest vision rushes through my head. It seems like the driver has been through a similar situation before. It looks like he knows well that those who step through that door do not usually come back out quickly, or at all.

– *No please! Please. Just 5 minutes. Please, I beg.*

I was ready to offer the man all the cash I had on me.

– *Fine. I'll wait for just five minutes. After that, I will unload your luggage and leave.*

– *Thank you.*

I walk inside the large rectangular hall with a long counter lining its entire back wall. One soldier is sitting toward the right looking down, probably reading.

– *Um… Hello. I am Ibrahim Lahoud. You asked to see me?*

– *Sit!* barks the soldier without even looking up.

– *I am sorry sir, but I can't stay. The taxi is waiting for me.*

– *Sit!*

– *Sir, please, if you only tell me what is wrong.*

– *I said sit!* threatens this time the soldier, raising his head and looking me straight in the eyes.

This is it, I think to myself, this is the end.

I heard many stories of abductions at the border with Syria. Now, it looks like I get to witness one, first hand. And the taxi… Are the 5 minutes over yet? Has he left? I start praying to St. Rita; Dad used to always implore her when in trouble. St. Rita de Cascia is the patron of lost and impossible causes.

– *What's going on?*

I am suddenly shaken out of my dark thoughts by the voice of a higher-ranking official stepping inside the room behind the soldier. The soldier whispers few words to him:

– *Give him a pass and send him downtown.*

That must be good news. The taxi should still be here, and I get to continue my journey to Damascus.

– *Take this paper; go to Damascus.*

The soldier throws the paper at me and I catch it in flight, and before even reading it I run out to meet the taxi. The driver is already unloading my luggage. Right on time.

On the way to Damascus, I fire up my lighter and read

the little yellow paper given to me. It states that I have to report to the *"Moukhabarat"* (Secret Service) Center Nº507. I am not allowed to leave the country before doing so. The taxi driver notices my anxiety and inquires about the issue. I tell him what the paper said.

– Don't worry, once we reach Damascus, I will introduce you to another driver friend of mine. He will take care of you, explains the man. *These things happen. All will be fine 'Inchallah'* (God Willing).

We reach the Syrian capital at 5:30 a.m. At the taxi station, the driver introduces me to his friend, Rashad, who reads the paper and asks around for the location of the Center Nº507, which happens to be close by. We get into Rashad's Toyota and drive there. We reach it 10 minutes later, only to find out that it is still closed. We are told that it will open at 7:00 a.m; it is 5:55 a.m.

Rashad drives me to a nearby grocery shop owned by a friend. He asks the old man to take care of me until he picks me up again. The welcoming owner offers me a cheese sandwich, and when I ask for a pack of Marlboros, he pulls it out from the meat chiller, hidden behind rows of beef cuts. All imported commodities are forbidden in Syria. Everybody relies on contraband; even bread is smuggled from Lebanon.

The wait is endless. I just sit there watching Damascus wake up, the streets getting busier, school buses driving by, and housewives dropping by the old man's grocery to shop for the day. As I look at my watch every few minutes, I start thinking of home, Mom, and Aline. Is this how it will end? I don't want to die here; worse, I don't want to "stay" here. Stories are abundant about the infamous "Mazze" prison in Damascus, where hundreds of Lebanese are being held and tortured.

At 6:50 a.m., Rashad comes back and leads me to the Intelligence Center. I display my yellow paper to the sentry who tells me to step in, alone. I look at Rashad.

– *Don't worry, Mr. Ibrahim,* he says. *I'll be waiting here for you with your luggage. I'm not going anywhere. I promise.*

I skeptically smile and disappear into the dark corridor. I reach an open door with another sentry who pushes me by the shoulder.

– *Sit there.*

It's a small kitchen with two couches set at a right angle. A window with iron bars casts some light at an incredibly filthy sink filled with dirty teacups and glasses. On the couches are two Syrians, a young man in his thirties and the other in his mid-fifties. The latter man is crying. As I sit between the two men, he starts telling how worried he is about his life. It seems a cousin of his who was brought here a week ago, has never been seen or heard of since. The man is crying scared over his own fate. I just sit there and start praying; I never prayed so much in my life. I felt ashamed of myself, seeking God's help now that I needed Him most. I think of how oblivious I have been of His presence when things were right. We all treat God more as an insurance policy, a free one.

I remain in the kitchen for about 2 more agonizingly endless hours, then:

– *Ibrahim!* someone yells from the other end of the corridor.

– *Yes,* I reply standing up.

I walk toward the entrance of the kitchen where the soldier calling my name dives on me and rudely pushes me back in the kitchen.

– *You come only when we call you.*

I should have guessed; half of Arab men are called Ibrahim. As it happens, the younger man in the kitchenette also carries my name. I was wondering why he followed me when I stood up.

It is now 1:00 p.m. Six hours have passed since I sat on that couch. The same sentry comes a few feet away from the kitchen and shouts "Ibrahim" again. This time, I do not even dare to move. The sentry calls my name two more times and finally steps in the kitchen, looks me in the eye:

– *You are Ibrahim, right?*

– *Uuhh, yes I am,* I mumble with a barely audible voice.

– *And why aren't you answering you ass?!*

– *Sorry, but I did not know you were call...*

I did not finish my sentence. The soldier slaps me on the face, holds me from my shirt's shoulder, and shoves me in the corridor. He drags me into a large high-ceilinged room. That room sends chills down my spine. It reminds me so accurately of the early 70s war movies; vintage floor tiles, an old wooden rectangular table right in the center with an officer on one chair, and another empty chair facing him. A bare light bulb hanging all the way from the high ceiling reaching a couple of feet above the table casts a narrow beam of light that leaves the rest of the room in the dark. This is an interrogation room. The seated officer has a yellow file folder opened in front of him.

– *Sit,* he orders me, pointing with his chin at the chair facing him.

The soldier who brought me in by the shirt is still holding me, with the sleeve half-way up to my neck by now. He pulls me, throws me on the chair, and walks out of the room. Five minutes pass before the officer raises his head and start speaking.

– *Name?*

– *Ibrahim Nadim Lahoud.*

– *Nadim is your father's name?*

– *Yes sir, it is.*

– *Your mother's name.*

– *Nadia.*

– *Nadia what?*

– *Nadia Zeidan.*

And it goes on: religion, residence, phone numbers, schools I attended, marital status, city of origin, work, etc. After every question, he looks down at the folder in front of him, flipping papers as if comparing my answers to data he already had. Then came the question I feared the most:

– *Which political party do you belong to?*

My tongue goes numb. What kind of a question is that? I am a Christian, a Maronite, from the Chouf mountains, living in the Christian Keserwan. What political party do they think I could belong to? I knew that with all the information I provided, there was only one evident answer that officer was expecting. He was probably waiting just for that answer to send me into oblivion. I am supposed to reply that I belong to the Lebanese Forces, the Christian militia; which of course is not the case, but who would believe any other answer?

It takes me a second to react:

– *Excuse me? Can you repeat the question?*

The officer looked at me with a grin that clearly said *"Really? Do you want me to repeat that question?"*

I had to find an answer, and quick; an answer to save my neck.

– *I am a Red Cross certified first-responder. My serial number is 1428/102. Before I joined the Red Cross, I had to prove beyond any doubt that I didn't belong to any political party; otherwise, I would not have been accepted. You can call the International Red Cross and check my credentials.*

It is now almost 2:00 p.m. That was the last question. The officer calls the sentry. The door opens immediately and without further discussion, the soldier escorts me back to the same kitchen, where I wait until 4:00 p.m.

The same soldier returns and hands me a white piece of paper and asks me to leave. Just like that. It's over. I'm free. The piece of paper is a pass to leave the country.

I was sure that Rashad, the taxi driver has left with my luggage. To my delight, he is still outside standing by his car, smoking and waiting for me. He drives me to a nearby motel to spend the night. At the lobby, I ask the receptionist's help to call the Syrian Airlines and switch my flight to the next morning. I also call Jad to inform him of my one-day delay.

After my ordeal in Syria I land in Abu Dhabi, the capital and most westward city of the United Arab Emirates, where Jad is supposed to pick me up. We will have to drive for 5 hours to reach Fujairah, on the opposite side of the country. After a trouble-free 3-hour flight, I reach Abu Dhabi thinking that finally my life is back to normal. I am still traumatized by what happened in Damascus and worried about my return flight, which will have to be also via Damascus.

Jad told me that he would be waiting for me with the original copy of my visa behind the large glass wall separating the public from the passport check area. He will toss the visa over the wall, and I will use it to get through. He had faxed me a copy few days earlier.

Jad is not there. I scan the crowd looking for him, but he is nowhere to be found. *"Ok, it seems like the odyssey is not over yet,"* I think to myself. I wait and wait while the airport slowly drains of its passengers and welcomers, until I am the only one left standing behind the glass wall.

An officer walking by approaches me and asks what the problem is. I show him my visa faxed copy and tell him I am waiting for my brother who has the original copy. He nods and walks away. My heart is pounding; I look around for a public phone. There is not one there, and there is no other way I can reach Jad. Where could he be? Did I fly on the wrong date or wrong destination? This can't be happening. I start praying, telling God that I honestly think what happened in Syria should have been enough a punishment to absolve all my sins. This is when the officer shows up again:

– *Your brother did not come yet?*

– *No sir. But I am sure he's on his way.*

– We can't wait anymore. No visa, no entry.

He moves a few feet away, speaks on his radio for few seconds.

– The plane cannot wait anymore either. You have 5 minutes. After that, we will board you again back to Syria.

This trip, since I left Beirut, has proven to me beyond any doubt that God works in mysterious ways indeed. I must have sinned so bad in my life, He needed to teach me one hell of a lesson. As I am staring at the officer horrified and on the brink of cardiac arrest, I hear a muffled voice shouting my name. I look at the glass wall and see Jad running in and waving a piece of paper high up in the air, followed by another man.

– He's here, my brother is here, I shout in jubilation looking at the officer and back at Jad.

Jad and I get close to the glass wall. He smiles at me and tosses the visa over the wall. I catch it while still staring at him. My eyes are asking the question *"Where the fuck have you been?"*

– You have the visa? I am awakened from my silent rant by the officer's pressing tone.

– Yes, yes, Officer, here it is, I reply joyfully, waving the paper.

On our way to Fujairah, Jad explains to me that they had a flat tire and no spare. Half-way through our trip, the car's air conditioning system fails. It is 99 degrees outside with 100 percent humidity. We reach Fujairah finally around 6:00 p.m. As I am unloading my luggage it starts raining, something that seldom, if ever, happens at this time of the year. By 8:00 p.m., there's a sudden power cut, also something that "never" happens. I am starting to think that my odyssey has shifted to a curse, and I am the jinx.

My interview is in Dubai, in 2 days. The way things are evolving; I am expecting an earthquake or flood.

In retrospect, 102 has just paid me back for all my services. I saved many lives, and the Red Cross has just saved mine in Syria.

(Jad)
AND THE MIRACLE TO CREATE LIFE
1985

I wanted to get married at a young age and start a family of my own. This stemmed from my fear of dying young, like my dad, and not having enough time to raise my kids and be next to them when they grow up. Eby and I have witnessed firsthand what it's like to grow up without a father, and I pledged to myself to do everything in my power not let this happen to my own family.

After Josette and I got married and moved to Fujairah, we started trying to get pregnant. It was not working, and Josette was going through one miscarriage after the other. Disappointment followed by frustration were setting in, but not our resolve did not fail. We agree to fly to London where a pioneering procedure called "GIFT" sounded like the breakthrough we were waiting for. An hour or so through the procedure, one of the Doctors comes to the visitor's waiting room and informs me that they had to suspend the procedure. He and his team have discovered that Josette was already pregnant, and the embryo was stuck in one of her 2 Fallopian tubes, and dead... Talk about "gift"...

Now the medical team was asking for my consent to surgically cut her Fallopian tube and remove the deceased fetus, while working to save the tube. I had no choice. I agreed. The hardest part was breaking the shocking news to Josette when she came to after her general anesthesia.

Still, we did not give up. About 6 years later, we moved to the United States. Throughout the years, our yearning for children grew stronger and we kept trying. We explored any possible medical procedure avenue, including multiple in-vitro trials.

We were bordering on obsession, when I receive a letter from Josette's Doctor, with whom we had now become friends. In his letter, he was asking us to stop trying. Almost begging, he explained that Josette's body cannot take any more the physical stress of the procedures, and advised us to give up and simply accept the fait-accompli.

By that time, I was sitting on the Board of the Saint Jude Children's Research Hospital. For me, being part of this amazing endeavor was one way to compensate for a void I had in my own life. One day, after leaving the board meeting, I head to the St. Jude Thaddeus Chapel located on the premises. There, a book is kept for people to write prayers, wishes, and vows. I knelt and prayed for a moment before heading to that book to write a vow. I pledged that if I manage to adopt a baby boy, I will name him Jude; or if it's a girl, I will call her Joy-Jude.

Why adopt? Anthony Abraham is one of the founders of the Saint Jude Children's Research Hospital. He is a famous Lebanese-American Philanthropist living in Miami. Although much older than I, we nurtured a warm friendship. Anthony Abraham had adopted and raised five children from Lebanon, and was ready to assist me through the process by introducing me to the orphanage back in my home country and helping me with the adoption papers and legalities.

A couple of months later, Josette flew to Lebanon to

spend some time with her family and start exploring the adoption process and visit the orphanage. She called me from Beirut a few weeks after she arrived, telling me that she was around 3 weeks late... I interrupt her asking her to forget about it all. She cannot go through this anymore physically, and both of us can't go through it mentally and emotionally. We were afraid that it would be another ectopic pregnancy. She agrees, but not before insisting that, this time, she strongly felt it was different. I simply ask her to relax, enjoy her time with the family and focus on the adoption project, and, if she likes, to take a pregnancy test the next morning. Indeed, she was pregnant...

After eight miscarriages, it was another bittersweet "victory", one that forbade us from calling it a success or enjoying the moment. We have been there before, and with every failure our strength of will and exhilaration were being slowly eroded to the bone. Josette's woman's intuition was urging her to book a Doctor's appointment. She did, and the physician's first instinct was to perform an ultrasound scan.

Josette called me after her Doctor's visit to tell me that she was indeed pregnant, and it was a perfectly normal pregnancy so far, the first since we have started trying to have children 17 years ago.

Josette stayed 6 more days in Beirut before she began having nausea and wanted to see her home doctor in Miami. I called her supervising Doctor, the one who sent us a letter earlier asking us to stop trying and confront reality. He immediately asks me to call his office and book an appointment. Once at the clinic, he immediately performs an ultrasound scan on Josette. Halfway through the procedure, he stops, and I could see him tearing up.

He was not crying, but one could read the incredulous expression on his face. For a moment, I was scared:

– *What is it Michael? Something's wrong?*

– *No, not at all, he replies. It's just...*

– *Just what?* I ask, insisting.

– *Jad, I have been practicing for years. As a matter of fact, I teach Medicine. In our profession, there's nothing called a "miracle". We don't teach about "miracles". What am I going to tell my students now? Jad, this is a miracle – Josette is pregnant.*

Eight months and 1 week since that first phone call from Beirut, I kept my vow and called our newborn baby girl Joy-Jude.

No matter what religion you follow, or what you believe; two things are for sure. God works indeed in mysterious ways, and miracles do happen. And now, I can prove it.

(Eby)
ON THE BALCONY... AGAIN
1986

It was 4:30 p.m. on a November afternoon. It is getting colder. The country has switched to winter daylight saving time and it gets dark much earlier.

Nadia could notice the Sannine Mountains and the Jounieh bay turning into a dark orange here and there. It's very cloudy on the horizon and the streets are still wet from the early afternoon shower. The smell of the fresh wet soil fills her nostrils.

Nadia is standing on the balcony, leaning on the dusty light grey rail. Facing the Beirut Port, she is reciting her daily rosary, something she does ever since that day In 1972 when she lost her husband. Jad should be home soon now, followed by Eby.

A few days from now I will turn 28, and my wife and I are expecting our first baby. What a joy to become a grandmother for the first time! Nadia is dreaming of holding the baby. If it's a boy, we all agreed to call him Nadim, after my Dad. He will carry on the family name. Nadia realizes that the whole Lahoud family legacy stands on her sons' and one cousin's shoulders. If we all have girls, the family is extinct.

She's alone, so alone. Her children are thousands of miles away. The wide turbulent dark blue sea laced with white foamy stripes of waves waltzing in the wind, the dark clouds building intricate layers of shapes and stories, the mountains shrouded with fog casting majesty over the scenery, the empty wet streets... That is all she has left; the only things that did not leave.

This is it. The famous balcony that nurtured our dreams and hopes Jad and I. Mom was waving at us that day in the early 2000's when we came for a visit.

(Eby)
THE DUBAI SHUFFLE
1986

Dubai will prove to be the turning point in my life; a full 180º turn. Dubai made me realize that it only takes one bold move in your life for a snowball effect to take place. It also taught me that a bold move does not have to be a radical one – just bold enough.

After conducting an interview with the advertising agency in Dubai, I get hired. I return to Beirut to wait for the issuance of my residence visa. Flying back home through Syria was as flawless as it was scary. My residence visa is finally issued 2 months later, in December. I will start my new job as a Creative Director in Dubai on January 1986.

I have been in advertising now for a little less than a decade. This agency in Dubai turned into the epiphany that triggered the 180º shift in my professional life. Apple Computer's regional head office is one of our clients. Their offices are located on the ground floor, while mine are on the ninth floor of the same office tower on the beautiful Dubai Creek. During the lunch breaks, which extend from 1:00 p.m. to 4:00 p.m., I stayed at work fiddling with a first-generation Apple Macintosh provided to the agency by the client. I fell in love, and the management at Apple noticed.

One day in January of 1987, I get a call from Jack, the Managing Director of Apple asking to see me. *"Right away,"* I reply, thinking he needed to discuss the current advertising campaign we are working on. I take the elevator down to the ground floor and walk into Jack's office. He was having a coffee with his partner.

– *Good day, Ibrahim, have a seat,* says Jack.

Have a seat? For some reason it did not sound good. "Have a seat" is almost similar to "We have to talk". I sit while bouncing looks back and forth at him and his partner.

– *Are you happy at work?* he asks abruptly.

– *Umm, yeah, sort of. Why?* I reply with a fake smile.

– *I'll go straight to the point,* says Jack, *how about you come work for us?*

Long silence, eyes opened wide, lame face, hanging lower jaw; that summarizes my first reaction.

– *Work for you? You mean here at Apple?*

– Yes. We know how much you like the brand and products. We feel how dedicated you are to creating successful campaigns. So, my partner and I thought that you might as well join us and put all that creativity to work. What do you say?

– But, I am a Graphic Designer. What will I do here?

– You will be the Marketing Executive.

What? Wait a minute. Did I just hear "Marketing"? What's wrong with these people? I just mentioned that I am a Graphic Designer. How can I be a Marketing Executive?

– I have never worked in the marketing field. What makes you so sure I can do it? I reply, worried.

– I know you can do it. You have what it takes. I can tell. I know it's an important career decision, so think about it for a while, but I can tell you this: You will be on the client side, and you will be with Apple Computer. I will not be able to pay you more than what you already make; but you will grow as we grow, and the career rewards are immense, I can promise you that.

– I will think about it and answer you the soonest I can. Thank you very much for putting your trust in me. I leave.

That night, I did not sleep for a second. I discussed the offer with Aline and tried to weigh the pros and cons of the shift. There were no cons, not a single one; well, except making my current boss mad at Jad, because he referred me to him. I am so scared. Marketing, I do know well what it means. I lied to Jack. I can do marketing very well, my mind has always been geared toward it, and marketing has been steering my design career since I started.

The next morning, I call Jack and ask if I can see him. He

asks me to come down in 1 hour.

– *I thought about your offer all night.*

– *And?* he asks while twisting the hair of his thick grey mustache.

– *I'm in.*

– *Great. You give your agency the 1-month notice, while we work on your visa transfer. You start on February first.*

This was the shortest interview of my life and the biggest shift in my career; the 5 minutes that dictated my professional path since.

I spend 7 wonderful years at Apple Computer. There, I learn everything about branding, marketing, company culture, and philosophy. I also learn and witness the future firsthand, and it looks simply amazing.

While at Apple, I meet Abdo, the Creative Director at the new agency we appoint to handle Apple's account after I left advertising. It is mid-1991, and we slowly grow to become best friends. Abdo and I share the same passion for design, attention to detail, and creativity. We also share the same life interests, like movies – especially science fiction and documentary TV shows. As we get to be closer friends, we start discussing our careers and how to move forward.

After many brainstorm sessions at either my place or his, we agree to start our own business. It will be the first corporate identity and strategic design firm in the region. I manage to recruit the Director of Sales at Apple who will help us find the local partner, a mandatory condition for foreigners to start a business in the UAE. We work hard for 6 months until it finally comes to life. "IDentity" is born on September 1994, with its first office located in my garage.

What a beautiful metaphor to how Steve Jobs started Apple in his parent's garage.

"IDentity", during its short 4-and-a-half-year life span, makes history. We work on some of the most prestigious businesses in the country and the regions, and win numerous regional and International awards, the last of which comes to crown the firm's end in May 1999, The Dubai Quality Appreciation Award.

In February that year, a mutual friend of both Abdo and me shows up in Dubai on a short visit. He tells us that he has been working on a project back in Beirut. He is establishing a large multi-discipline communication holding that will be able to deal with any sort of client, of any size, and anywhere in the world. Both Abdo and I express our will to join in. "IDentity" has been going through rough times and Abdo and I were already discussing exit plans. Our friend's visit came at the perfect time. It was February 12, 1999.

On February 14, Valentine's Day, I take Aline out to dinner in a fancy restaurant and give her the good news. We are going back to Beirut. Our son Nadim is 12 years old and Sabine is only 2.

In June 1999, we move back to Beirut where I join the group my friend has started. No one is happier than my Mom.

That marks the end of my 13 years in Dubai, and the start of the third chapter of my life. After the Red Cross and my move to Dubai (where my career was sculpted and polished) it is time to move back to Lebanon and build on it, or so I hope. Twenty-seven years ago, Dad died and with him all my hopes. Seventeen years ago, I joined the Red Cross trying to inject some meaning into my life.

Fourteen years ago, I was a meager Designer in obscure agencies trying to make a living, never a career. Today, I am back with a "Regional Marketing Manager" title for the most sought-after computer maker in the world, and a "Managing Partner" title for the pioneering and most successful branding firm back then.

In December, I will turn 40. Perfect timing.

(Eby)
THAT BALCONY...
2012

As this story comes to a close, an event occurs that is a stark reminder to its beginning. History always repeats itself. In our case, Jad and I, it brings to closure two unfinished chapters in our life.

For over 20 years now, Jad has been living and working in Miami, Florida. He is married to Josette, my 102 teammate, and has a beautiful daughter, Joy-Jude, my only niece. As for me, after 13 years I am back in Lebanon from Dubai and a proud father of a boy and a girl.

Monday, April 2nd, 2012.

Two days earlier, I took Mom for a doctor's visit. She was suffering from severe stomach pain. The practitioner prescribed a medicine that should cure Nadia's pain. The drawback is that it might induce heavy drowsiness. As prevention, the doctor asks Mom to take the medicine at night before going to sleep and recommends that someone remains with her for the first 3 days. If the medicine does not cause any side effects, she will carry on with the treatments for 3 more weeks. Mom and I agree that she would start the cure on Monday, and I will spend the first 3 nights with her in Gemmayzeh.

I liked the idea of being back in my childhood room and bed; the same two beds Dad had had manufactured for Jad and me back in 1971, 1 year after we moved to the new home and just a year before he passed away. I can still remember our excitement and the smell of freshly lacquered wood. Dad had also installed a new small chandelier on the same evening and pasted flowery decals on the large light gray cupboards doors to brighten things up a little. Hardly anything has changed since, except the new blackout curtains and air conditioning unit that Jad installed to dim the light and keep the room cool in the hot summer days when he comes with the family from Miami to spend their vacation.

On Monday, after work, I drive to Mom's to spend the first night. I do not sleep much, staying alert to her moves. She is an insomniac – I inherited that from her. She leaves her bed numerous times at night; goes to the bathroom or grabs a snack. I stay awake most of the night watching over her.

The next morning, Nadia tells me that she did not feel any drowsiness. So far, it looks like the medicine is well-tolerated by her frail body.

The following night after work I go out with my closest friend, Abdo, for an after-hours coffee before driving again to Mom's to spend the second of the 3 nights. Same scenario; no sleep, Nadia going to the bathroom, taking a walk around the living room, or grabbing a snack of usually a banana. I did manage to get some sleep toward the early morning hours.

On Wednesday morning, before driving the short distance to work, I ask Mom if she felt any negative effects, and she says no. I am happy that she is tolerating the strong medicine. Nadia is in her 80s now and plagued by illnesses. Of the seven siblings in her large family, she had the weakest health. She has had countless surgeries, including the two caesarians to deliver Jad and me. She begs me to go home tonight, insisting that she is feeling great and ready to continue the treatment for the 3 prescribed weeks.

It is tempting. I miss my bed, my children, and the cool weather of Ajaltoun where I live now. I tell Mom that I will think about it. Later, I convince myself that 1 more night won't harm, and that I'd better finish what I started. Mom begs me again to go home. I refuse.

On that Wednesday night, Nadia sleeps very well. She snores so loud that I have to spend the night sleeping on my right side, covering my healthy ear. (Following a long exposure to cold wind during a scout camp field games, I had gradually lost most of the hearing in my left ear.) At times like tonight, it is a blessing and comes in handy.

On Thursday morning, at 6:00 a.m. sharp, I wake up and look at the time and decide I could easily sleep until 8:00 a.m. It only takes me 5 minutes to get to work, and I badly need the rest. A short while later, I hear Mom leaving her bed and entering the bathroom located in the small corridor separating the two bedrooms. If I bend over the bed, I could see her.

I hear the toilet flush, the door open, and Mom exiting. Then I hear the metallic sounds of a falling object. I lean over and see Nadia bending to grab her cane. She must have dropped it, I think to myself. I feel happy that she could bend and grab it. It's a good sign that she is regaining some of her physical fitness. I let my head fall again on the pillow.

Two more minutes pass, and once more I hear a strange sound; not metallic this time but muffled. I look again and see Mom on her hands and knees, on the rug next to her bed. She must have fallen but gently. That's why I heard the muffled sound. I jump out of bed and step into her room. She seems to be looking for something. I could see her cane now neatly stowed next to her bed where she always keeps it. I'm puzzled. What is she looking for?

– Come on Mom. Stand up.

I was ready to help her but wanted to see if she could make it alone first.

– I'mmmmm f-f-iiinnnnne, answers Nadia in a very strange mumble.

I immediately bend over her, place my hand on her shoulder and look at her. The left side of her face was inanimate. She is still mumbling but only the right side is moving. That's why I could not understand a word. My Red Cross training kicks in. I am not muscular and do not have the physical strength to carry heavy objects, but adrenaline rushes through my veins and miraculously grants me enough power to kneel, lift up my 143-pound (65-kg) Mom, and put her in bed.

I know what she suffers from, but I wanted to make sure first. I lift her left arm and let it go; it falls right back. I try her left leg. Same reaction. Her left eye is shut. She still tries to speak, but only the right side of her face moves and none of the words she tries to articulate are comprehensible.

I immediately rush to my room, pick up my cell phone and dial 102, now located exactly at the same level where we live, but on the upper street; where Jad used to work at our uncle's clothing shop. I get dressed while giving instructions to the lady on the phone, about our location and Mom's situation. I hang up and rush back to Nadia.

She's barely awake and moving. All I manage to hear is her trying to tell me she's fine and there is no need to go to hospital. I think how strange that is. How could she not feel what's wrong with her? I hold her arm, with my fingers on her pulse, and notice that it is slowly dropping. I could barely feel it now. I start to panic. I try to check the pulse on her inner thigh. I feel the beating, but it is irregular and very faint. I run again to the balcony, waiting for the ambulance, which arrives in another 5 minutes. I wave at them, indicating the fifth floor with my open hand, and rush to the intercom to open the building's main gate. It is 6:18 a.m.

Nadia is rushed to the St. George Hospital's Emergency Center. She has a cerebral thrombosis in her right lobe. She spends 2 days in intensive care. She miraculously recovered from the thrombosis with almost no side effects. This is due to my and 102's quick reaction time. It was Friday.

On Saturday morning, I arrive to the hospital at 7:00 a.m. Mom is about to be moved from Intensive Care and into a room. I find out that, overnight, she had developed a psychosis. It's a post-traumatic syndrome caused by the shock of being in intensive care or after receiving anesthetics. Patients become delusional and lose their sense of time and space. Nadia thinks she's home and is waiting for her sisters Isabelle and Marie-Rose to come for their usual morning coffee. She barely recognizes me; and when she does, she gets angry with me, thinking I am keeping her from leaving.

I have been under so much pressure the past week, and that is the last thing I need. The nurses reassure me that psychosis is very common and it usually recedes within 24 to 48 hours. Nadia is moved to a room on the eighth floor. I am in constant contact with Jad who is worried sick, filling him in on the latest developments.

Nadia gets worse. Her psychosis degenerates and she is now completely out of sync with reality. I spend the day with her and leave around 8:00 p.m. for home. This is supposed to be my first night home. Since she started taking the prescribed medicine, I have been sleeping with her. When she was moved to hospital, I kept sleeping at her place, which is quite close to the hospital. I reach home around 8:30 p.m., greet everyone and walk into my bedroom to change and get ready for dinner. As I am putting my computer case on the floor my phone rings. It's the hospital. Mom keeps trying to leave her bed, and they cannot allocate a nurse to stay with her in the room all the time. They ask me to come back and stay with her. It is Saturday night and traffic is unbearable at this hour; everyone is going out. I pick up my stuff and immediately head back to the hospital. It takes me 45 minutes to reach it. I enter the hospital from the Emergency access; all other doors are locked for the night. I reach the eighth floor and walk inside Mom's room. She is on the floor, with blood everywhere. The nurses are trying to place her back in bed. While trying to leave her bed, she fell on the floor and tore the IV pipe from her forearm sending blood gushing.

Three more days pass, and on the fourth, after numerous tests, the doctors conclude that she has contracted a severe urinal tract infection. Her white cell count has skyrocketed, causing the psychosis. Had they not diagnosed the situation, things might have gotten worse. An intense antibiotics treatment is immediately initiated through intravenous injections.

Fort the past 4 days, I lived in a permanent state of

panic. I was watching my Mother slipping out of my hands and could not do a thing about it. I was also worried about Jad, trying to give him the essential news only and avoiding worrying him further. Nadia did not sleep or stop talking for the whole 3 days and nights. Her body has lost most of its strength. She looks skinny with vacant eyes. She barely eats. Something is telling me this was the end.

On the fifth morning, Tuesday, Nadia wakes up at 9:30 a.m. It was the first time that she sleeps for 5 hours straight. For me, this is a good sign.

– *Good morning my love,* she says.

That is all I needed to hear; Mom is back! The antibiotics treatment worked. We talk and talk. Nadia is wondering where she had been all that time.

– *It feels like I was somewhere else. I don't remember a thing. How long have we been here?*

– *Six days now Mom.*

I turn my head toward the window and start crying.

Nadia spends another 4 days at the hospital, a total of 10 days. She leaves on Sunday morning for home. She refuses to be taken by ambulance. She rides with me.

I manage, with the help of Jad's close friend Christian, to find a housekeeper to come and stay with Nadia. I spend 2 more nights with her. On Monday, it is the first time I sleep in my bed in Ajaltoun since the beginning of April. It was now the 16th.

Jad arrives in Beirut on Friday the 20th. He could not help it. He had to see Mom. The last time he saw her was back in 2009. We all spend the weekend together with the family. Mom never looked better.

On Monday morning, Nadia's feet swell disproportionately and look like elephant feet. Her blood pressure climbs to a dangerous level. We call the doctor, who asks to readmit her promptly to the hospital. She spends another 3 days there until the swelling recedes. She is discharged without anyone ever finding out why her feet were swollen. The common explanation is that it's due to her previous hospital stay.

Back home, we tuck Mother in bed and we step on the balcony. That small space of 20 feet by 5 feet overlooking the mountain and the sea became a shrine, a meditation and council space. On that balcony dreams, tears, hope, and hopelessness were forged. There, Jad and I have a long talk, exploring the remaining options to insure Mom's well-being. None was found, so we make a crucial decision. With her deteriorating health and an emerging recurring health pattern, Mom can no longer live alone in Gemmayzeh, not even with a housekeeper or a nurse. The house is not well-equipped to handle her case, continuous medical attention is not available, and if anything happens late at night on a Friday, it will take the ambulance hours to reach her. Gemmayzeh became the prime nightlife spot of Beirut. Weekends, starting Friday nights, are a nightmare. Traffic jams, lack of parking spaces, and unbearable noise plague the neighborhood. Nadia will never make it to the hospital on time.

It is decided that Nadia will leave her Gemmayzeh home for good and relocate to "Longue Vie", the best and most exclusive nursing home for the elderly available in Lebanon.

Jad and I have already done our homework, investigating all available options. The first and foremost concern is to find a wonderful place to live with constant medical attention. "Longue Vie" is the only facility that answers both criteria.

Nadia has always been an amazing woman. Easy to communicate with, she accepts realities and admits the necessities. She agrees willingly to go to "Longue Vie", but she never realizes that it would be for good. We decide not to discuss it with her for now, for her own good. The date is set for the next morning, Thursday, April 26, 2012.

In the afternoon, while her sisters are helping her pack and get ready to leave early the next morning to "Longue Vie", Mom feels dizzy and falls. Luckily, Jad is standing right behind her and manages to catch her before she hits the ground. She only scratches her elbow. Jad helps her sit on a chair next to her bed. Seconds later, she starts fainting, her eyes roll back, and she turns cold.

I help Jad carry her to bed and start checking her pulse. Jad slaps her twice on the face, a technique learned at 102. We are both scared to death. Treating a stranger is one thing; attending to a close family member is a totally different story.

She slowly wakes up and remains in bed. That night, Jad sleeps next to her in bed so he can closely monitor her vitals. I desperately need a good night sleep.

On Thursday morning, Jad, Mom, and I wake up very early. A long time ago, at the end of every school year with the beginning of summer, we used to move to Jouret el Termos in the Keserwan mountains to spend the summer. I remember the thrill of waking up very early with Jad on that day, waiting for the truck to arrive and load furniture and luggage. This morning, it almost feels the same, but without the thrill. Nadia is leaving her home of 42 years for good.

Three of us sit and have one last coffee in the dining room. Jad and I check one last time for any item that we forgot to pack. I start roaming every room, closely looking at every piece of furniture. In the maid's room, there's the cupboard from our childhood. This yellow closet dates back from the early 60s when we were still living in the old Gemmayzeh home. Dad had decals of gazelles and birds stuck on every door. Now Mom uses it as storage for all the clothes she does not use anymore. In the kitchen, the concrete frame of what was once a window still stands, a witness for the day a mortar fell and hit the kitchen and our bedroom. On the small kitchen balcony are Mom's little babies: her plants and flowers. I am sure that these little green wonders kept my Mom sane for all these lonely years she spent alone at home.

Her room is the hardest to look at. I love the smell every time I step in; a mixture of talcum powder, hand cream, and lavender cologne bestows a peaceful feeling. Her dresser is always neatly organized with hairbrushes to the left, accessories to the right, and perfumes in the middle. The mirror is scattered with little black and white photos of family.

"Longue Vie" allows residents to use their own furniture to decorate their rooms. So, the day before Jad and I made a list of items we will ship the next morning. A small dresser with a mirror that was placed in our bedroom, Mom's bed with its bedside table, two wood and canvas chairs from the living room, a couple of Persian rugs, the TV, a bookshelf that's hanging in the corridor near the bathroom, most of her Barbara Cartland books, and a lot of photos in frames.

I am still standing in Mom's bedroom. In this room, Dad died and Mom almost died. In this room, I saw my first dead human. In this room, Jad and I found comfort for years. Tears fill my eyes, but do not fall. They just stay there as if it is forbidden to cry anymore in this house.

I walk back to the dining room where Jad and Mom are still sitting on the sofa that witnessed years of my Mom's lonely days go by.

– *Let's take one last photo. The last photo in our house,* Jad says. And so, we did. We take two photos that immortalize the end of 42 years of tears, laughs, fear, and weddings.

We leave for Bhersaf, where "Longue Vie" is located. Mom is with me in the car, and Jad follows us in Christian's car. We are met there by Aline and the children; and we arrive to a warm welcome from the manager and the team of nurses and caretakers. Mom is taken to room 209. In the afternoon, Jad and I, with the help of Christian, hire a small truck and transport the furniture from Mom's home to her room at the nursing home.

By 5:00 p.m. Nadia's room looks like a miniature replica of her home in Gemmayzeh. This plays a very important role in her accepting the new situation.

Nadia has been at "Longue Vie" for almost a month. Jad is back to Miami and me to work. Since 2000, this is the first time we feel that Mom is safe and in good hands.

Nadia has had a thrombosis. Just like my Dad. She was in bed, just like my Dad. I was alone at home with her, just like with my Dad. What were the odds?

Three miracles occurred that day. I was sleeping at Mom's. I woke up at 6:00 a.m. without any apparent reason. She fell right next to her bed. Had she continued sleeping she would have died, just like Dad.

The two closures? First, I was given a second chance by God. I saved my Mother from the same illness and in the very same situation as my Dad.

The second closure is about 102 paying my brother and me back for all that we both did during those 5 years at the Red Cross. Our training helped save our Mother.

Also, she was attended to by 102's newest young recruits and carried in the famous 178 ambulance.

In August 2012 the house in Gemmayzeh is empty and will be vacated for good. The remaining furniture was given away to charity and the church. Jad has already left back for Miami and taken with him few items as souvenir, and I did too.

I take a final walk around the empty house while shooting a video on my cell phone. I do not want to forget our home nor any of the emotions associated with it. Only memories will remain bound to the walls. The smell of fresh lacquered wood on our new beds, the sound of the TV set delivering the news, the aroma of fresh Turkish coffee in that small room adjacent to the kitchen, and the echo of the chilling scream of that February day in 1972: *"Nadiiiiiiiiiiim"*.

Forty-two years later, year for year, our closure is done. On that balcony, Nadia will no longer stand waiting for her sons, smoking her cigarette, and reciting her rosary. Jad will not watch the planes over Beirut while dreaming of becoming a pilot. I will not wait for Dad to wake up from his nap. All in all, in some way, our lives have been dictated by that balcony. The path is long still; but for whatever it's worth, what we both did so far, we have done with our bare hands. We might not be successful yet, we might not be self-made, but we are surely "in-the-making".

(Eby)
HISTORY'S ABRUPT HALT
2015

Thursday, April 30, 2015 - 9:00 a.m.

Sabine, my daughter turned 18 in January. Today is her last day of school, ever. The Jesus and Mary School is organizing a celebration day for all the graduating students. It is a custom for departing pupils to celebrate that day in big fanfare. Speeches, printed T-shirts for the occasion, running around the school and classes, screaming, and throwing water balloons on each other are all part of the ritual.

Sabine left home earlier to join her classmates, while Aline and I follow at 8:15 a.m., each in our own car. Sabine had a long day ahead, and Aline decides to wait for her while I would drive back home. I took the day off and tomorrow is Friday, Labor Day. I am looking forward to a long peaceful weekend, only interrupted by my Saturday university classes.

As we reach Antelias and make an exit toward Rabieh, where the school is located, my iPhone buzzes. It's "Longue Vie", where my Mother has been for exactly 3 years this May. It's Shirine, The head nurse.

– She's vomiting again. Same symptoms as the two previous times. I'm not going even to ask for your permission. We're transferring her immediately to the hospital.

This is the third time we have had to admit Mom to the hospital suffering from an intestinal occlusion, a condition where the intestine forms a knot that prevents food from being processed and flushed through the digestive system. All three times happened at roughly the same interval, two months. The first couple of times, the occlusion miraculously untied by itself. The first time, Mom spent 3 days in the hospital. The second she spent a week, out of which 2 days were in Intensive Care. Both times, she went back to "Longue Vie" in perfect health.

Every time I receive a phone call from "Longue Vie", I get stomach cramps. They never call just to say hello.

– OK. I reply to Shirine, *I'm on my way. Text me when the ambulance picks Mom up.*

I call Aline, driving her car in front of mine, and get her up to speed. I thought that waiting for the ambulance to pick up my Mother might buy me some time to attend at least the beginning of the school ceremony.

We reach the school and enter the amphitheater. Sabine is beautiful in her school uniform and sitting to our right. I message her about the situation and tell her how sorry I am for having to miss the day I have been waiting 12 years for. She glances at me from her seat while typing on her phone telling me that she understands and asks me not to worry.

Someone is giving a presentation about safe driving. I decide to wait until it's over and leave, even if I do not hear from "Longue Vie". I don't have to wait much longer. Shirine sends me a text message telling me that the ambulance has just picked up Mom and left. The presentation ends 5 minutes later. I give Sabine a hug and kiss and leave.

The hospital is located near the school; it only takes me 10 minutes to reach it. I park and run toward the Emergency entrance. Mom has been four times to that hospital already during her 3-year stay at "Longue Vie". I know the layout and most of the staff. Even the Parking Attendant, Milad, became a friend.

I reach the Emergency and go straight into the room where Mom is waiting. The moment I see her, I have an ominous feeling. This time is different. Although the symptoms are similar to the last two times, something in her eyes, her face, her expression, is just not right.

I wait until she is transferred to a room on the third floor, where the procession of nurses and doctors starts. I stay with her until the evening and go home. It's just another intestinal occlusion, which will untie itself by tomorrow, or so the doctor says

One hour after reaching home, I receive a phone call from the hospital informing me that Mom needs to be operated on, but they will wait until tomorrow to see how things develop.

It is Friday, the 1st of May, Labor Day. I reach the hospital early in the morning and wait for the doctor who shows up around 10:30 a.m. He informs me that they inevitably have to operate. Mom's condition has worsened over time and her intestines have become badly convoluted inside her abdominal cavity. I am also told that the risks of not operating are equal to, or maybe even greater than the risk of an operation. In both cases, they estimate a 60-40 probability. What can I do except agree? Deep inside, I did fully agree. It is already taking a heavy toll on her health and, yes once more, this time did not feel right.

Nadia is operated at noon and transferred to intensive care for recovery and monitoring. She stays there until

Monday before being moved to a room on the fifth floor. While in Intensive Care, she once more develops an "ICU psychosis", where patients become delusional and start hallucinating. She suffered from that same syndrome 3 years ago when she had her thrombosis.

While quite worried, I was hoping the psychosis would fade away quickly this time, now that she is out of the Intensive Care. The days go by and, while still deep into her psychosis, Mom's health improves slowly as she starts eating solid food.

It is now Friday, May 8; and I have a very important meeting at the office at 3:00 p.m. I decide to visit Mom in the morning and then drive to the office for the meeting. I have not been to work since she was admitted, 8 days ago. I also decide to go to university the next morning. My Masters students cannot afford to skip classes anymore.

Mom does not look well. Her psychosis seems to be worsening, and her eyes have an eerie empty stare. She looks at me but does not see me. She mumbles incomprehensible words. The nurse blames it on the increased sedative dose. Reluctantly, I have to take that for an answer.

I give Mother a kiss on the forehead, hoping she can feel my presence, and leave.

Saturday, I go to my university classes. I call the hospital between classes to check on her and am told that she is stable. This relieves some of the guilt of not being with her.

I return home late in the afternoon, exhausted and drained. The past week has taken a heavy toll on both my physical and mental health. I can imagine how frustrated Jad must feel, being so far away and helpless. I had called him the same day Mother was admitted to hospital. Since then, he calls me at least twice a day to check on her, but mostly to check on me. He is riddled with the guilt of not being with us and worried a lot about me. He keeps insisting on flying to Beirut to be with us. I tell him that it is unnecessary and try to reassure him by telling him that Mom will be out by Monday, knowing it does not bring much solace.

I watch some TV, grab a quick dinner, and head to bed. I have to wake up early and go see Mom. The Doctor told me that tomorrow, Sunday, should be her last day at hospital. Monday morning, she will return to "Longue Vie" where she can complete her recovery and hopefully get over with her digestive problems.

I can't sleep that night; not a single second. I was running on empty, yet incapable of closing my eyes. I get out of bed at 2:00 a.m., get a glass of water, fiddle a little with my phone, and head back to bed hoping to get some sleep. The last time I looked at the time it was 3:45 a.m. I must have fallen asleep by then.

I wake up to Aline nudging my shoulder and whispering that my phone is buzzing. I usually put my iPhone on "Do Not Disturb" until 6:00 a.m. If an unknown number calls twice in a row, the phone will start ringing. And it was. By the time I grab my phone to answer, the person on the other end hangs up. I copy the phone number and check it on the TrueCaller app and I get Mom's hospital. I look at the time. It is 5:20 a.m.

This cannot be good. My heart starts pounding in my chest and my hands are shaking. I get out of bed and lean my forehead against the balcony door's glass that overlooks Beirut. I redial. No answer. I call the hospital's landline, inform them who I am and they immediately transfer me to the third floor ward. A man on the other end bluntly tells me:

– *Your mother is dead, may her Soul Rest in Peace.*

– *What?* I ask.

I did hear well the first time, but I needed to ask. The man repeats the same sentence, with the same detached tone of voice. I hesitate for 2 seconds and ask about the cause of death. *"Cardiac arrest,"* he replies without any further clarification.

In an odd epiphany, the first thing that comes to my mind is me insisting on Jad few days ago not to come to Beirut to see our mother. I am overwhelmed with guilt, fear, and utter sadness. I just denied my brother the right to have a last look at our mother, to give her one last kiss, one final hug. Jad had not seen our mother since the summer of 2013.

I hang up my phone and remain standing against the balcony door, head down. I hear Aline, who is still sitting in bed, asking:

– *What? What is it? What is it Eby?*

I slowly turn my head and look at her. She already had tears in her eyes. The reason is obvious. I keep staring at her. My tears are bursting uncontrollably. I am not crying, but tears fall abundantly down my cheeks. I try to speak but couldn't. That knot in my throat is holding back the words.

– *Nadia is dead. Mami is dead.*

I could hear Aline sobbing while I get dressed. I

immediately dial my cousin Johnny's mobile number. It's 5:25 a.m. Johnny is our maternal Aunt Isabelle's son. Although older than Jad and me, we always had a strong bond. We used to live in the same building in Gemmayzeh before we had to move due to Dad's stroke. We also used to spend summers together in Jouret El Termos village and again in the same building.

– *Hi, Hanoon* (Arabic nickname for John that also means "compassionate"), *sorry to bother you this early.*

– *Hi, Barhoom. No worries, habibi* (my dear), *what's wrong?*

– *Nadia is dead. I can't think of anyone else to call. I don't know what to do.*

– *Take it easy. I'll meet you at the hospital.*

I hang up and immediately, call Jad while still getting dressed. I try to rehearse how to break the news and what to say. You can never rehearse how to tell someone their mother died.

– *Hi, habibi,* says Jad. I could feel anxiety in his voice. It was around 10:30 P.M. in Miami. Why would I call this early from Beirut? *What's wrong?*

– *Jado... Mom... She, she passed away.*

A short silence. Jad, very composed, answers:

– *When?*

– *They called me just now from the hospital. I'm sorry Jado. I'm so sorry.*

Jad's voice is barely audible by now. He is gasping while trying to speak.

– Sorry for what? I will work on my bookings and keep you informed. I will call you in a while. Take it easy, Eby. I love you. She is in a better place. She's with Dad.

– Yes. She is finally with Nadim. We'll talk soon.

I hang up. Today is Mother's Day in the United States.

What I did not know is that Jad is having dinner in Miami when I called. Joy-Jude and he agreed to surprise Josette and take her out to celebrate. It is 5:36 a.m. in Beirut, 10:36 p.m. in Miami. Jad and his family are ready to order dessert when my photo appears on his ringing phone. For us, Mother's Day will never be the same...

It is 7:10 a.m. and Johnny is discussing the funeral service details with the mortician in Gemmayzeh, while I step outside the shop located less than 500 feet from our home on Pasteur Street. The neighborhood is still fast asleep on that Sunday morning. It feels like the countryside; birds are chirping and I can hear the morning breeze play hide and seek with the sycamore trees lining the street. It is so serene that I could easily forget why I am here. I light up a Café-Crème cigarillo, take a long puff, and look to my right. There, I see our building and the balcony on the fifth floor. I see Mom reciting her rosary waiting for us to come home.

That balcony was the incubator of our dreams and the place where war ruptured our inner peace.

EPILOGUE

Tuesday, May 12, 2015 - 12:30 p.m.

Jad and I are standing at Mom's grave. We are officially orphans. I realize now that there is no age to become an orphan, just as there is no age to the amount of love one has for his or her parents. We are and will always remain children, little children when parents are involved.

The pain of losing a father or mother does not really grow lesser with time. It grows stronger. It is our acceptance of death, as we grow wiser, and the hard facts of life that make the pain seem lesser. When you are faced with the reality of death, everything is dwarfed. Only the pain and love are magnified. Only the pain and love.

The reasons that brought Jad and me to the Red Cross, are the same that motivated us to write this story. They are the same reasons that still make us see all the disparate realities as one ultimate entity. Pain and love.

We are the children of war, true, but we had a choice. Whether we had a taste of the alternatives or not, we still feel that we made the right decision. The love of others, of each other, and of family, is a wealth that Jad and I will carry for life.

Some might agree, and some might not. Some will see their lives reflected in our story, and some will feel the distance we've always had between them and us. Whatever the outcome, it will remain a lesson to all of us; that no matter what you think, there always will be a "what if". It makes no difference how your life starts, but rather how you live it from there on. You see, it is never about the destination. It is about the journey.

This is the priceless legacy that we leave to Nadim, Sabine, and Joy-Jude, our children; a legacy that, for a change, we encourage them to spend; a legacy that grows from within, and one that grows the more you spend.

It is a legacy that needs no written will.

THE END

CONTENTS

Message to our dear readers. What is 102? 13
Prologue 15
Of fathers, trams and courage, *1950.* 18
(Eby) An end and a beginning. Living as an orphan, *1972.* 21
(Eby) A peace stranger than life, *1973* . 26
(Jad) Stranger in my own home, *1972.* 29
(Eby) Planning a life and making it work, *1978.* 33
(Jad) At war with myself, *1976.* 36
(Eby) To the red cross, and reconciliation with *life, 1981.* 47
(Eby) 102, *1982.* 54
(Eby) No more suicide missions for me, *1982.* 59
(Eby) The "sanafer", *1982.* 64
(Eby) The spare time of misfits, *1982.* 67
(Eby) Of delta, sleeping beauties and bomb shells, *1982.* 72
(Jad) Sheikh bashir, *1982.* 85
(Jad) Sabra, Chatila, and revenge, *1982.* 94
(Jad) M.A.S.H., *1983.* 106
(Eby) M.A.S.H. 2, *1983.* 110
(Jad) Burgers and bumpers, *1983.* 134
(Eby) Food fit for kings, *1983.* 137
(Jad) Echo of Souk el Gharb, *1983.* 141
(Eby) The helicopter transfer, *1983.* 146
(Jad) The talisman, *1983.* 156
(Jad) At the morgue, *1983.* 159
(Eby) A real ER, *1983.* 163
(Jad) CPR... at any cost, *1983.* 173
(Jad) A gift of life..., *1983.* 177
(Jad) The one-man outpost, *1983.* 186
(Eby) Cheating death, *1984.* 194
(Jad) Bozo made everyone cry, *1984.* 200
(Eby) Sierra, the silent warrior, *1984.* 207
(Eby) Antennae and snipers, *1984.* 217
(Eby) A pint for a life, *1984.* 224
(Eby) Two inches is all you need, when life is at stake, *1984.* 231

(Eby) The engagement, *1984.* 236
(Eby) Weddings and tears, *1985.* 239
(Jad) The Fujairah roller coaster, *1985.* 242
(Eby) The miracle of winning your life back, *1985.* 255
(Jad) And the miracle to create life, *1985.* 267
(Eby) On the balcony... again, *1986.* 271
(Eby) The Dubai shuffle, *1986.* 273
(Eby) That balcony..., *2012.* 279
(Eby) History's abrupt halt, *2015.* 292
Epilogue 300